Nelson Advanced Modular Science

Cell Biology & Genetics

JOHN ADDS • ERICA LARKCOM • RUTH MILLER

Thomas Nelson and Sons Ltd
Nelson House Mayfield Road
Walton-on-Thames Surrey
KT12 5PL UK

© John Adds, Erica Larkcom, Ruth Miller 1996
First published by Thomas Nelson and Sons Ltd 1996

I(T)P Thomas Nelson is an International Thomson Publishing Company

I(T)P is used under licence

ISBN 0-17-448266-3
NPN 9 8 7 6 5 4 3 2

Team Acknowledgements
Administration: Jenny Goode
Acquisitions: Chris Coyer
Concept Design: Maria Pritchard
Editorial Management: Simon Bell/Sharon Jordan
Marketing: Jane Lewis
Production: Liam Reardon

Designed and illustrated by Ian Foulis & Associates, Saltash, Cornwall

Printed in China

Contents

CONTENTS

Introduction

As modularisation of syllabuses gains momentum, there is a corresponding demand for a modular format in supporting texts. The Nelson Advanced Modular Science series has been written by Chief Examiners and those involved directly with the A level examinations. The books are based on the ULEAC (London) AS and A level modular syllabuses in Biology and Human Biology, Chemistry and Physics. Each module text offers complete and self-contained coverage of all the topics in the module. The texts also include examples outside the prescribed syllabus to broaden your understanding and help to illustrate the principle which is being presented. There are practical investigations and regular review questions to stimulate your thinking while you read about and study the topic. Finally, there are typical examination questions with mark schemes so that you can test yourself and help you to understand how to approach the examination.

The first text in the Biology series, *Cell Biology and Genetics*, looks at the fundamentals of Biology – at cells and their structures, at important molecules and how they are involved in metabolic pathways or the chemical reactions within living organisms. You will read about DNA and unravel the story of the coded information it contains about what living organisms are and how they work, and how this information is passed from one generation to the next. As we progress through the series, we develop a number of important biological themes: what goes on inside living organisms, how whole living organisms interact with each other and with their environment, and the way people use and exploit living organisms in their everyday lives. The authors hope that the books will give you a lively understanding of the subject and that you enjoy your study of Biology.

The authors

Erica Larkcom B.A., M.A., C. Biol., Subject Officer for A level Biology, formerly Head of Biology, Great Cornard Upper School, Suffolk

John Adds B.A., C.Biol., M.I.Biol., Dip. Ed., Chief Examiner for A level Biology, Head of Biology, Abbey Tutorial College, London

Ruth Miller B.Sc., C.Biol., M.I.Biol., Chief Examiner for AS and A level Biology, formerly Head of Biology, Sir William Perkin's School, Chertsey, Surrey

Acknowledgements

The authors and publishers would like to thank the following for permission to reproduce copyright material.

Artwork and text
The Open University for Figure 4.9, adapted from S102 A Science Foundation Course, Unit 2, *Biochemistry,* page 47, published by The Open University 1988
Philip Harris Biological Ltd for Figure 6.27, adapted from *Using Tribolium for Practical Genetics*, published in 1977
William C. Brown Publishers, for Figure 7.6, adapted from page 47 of Weaver, R. F. and Hedrick, P. W. *Genetics* 2nd edition, 1989

Photographs
Science Photo Library: Figures 1.1(a), 1.1(b), 1.2(a), 1.3, 1.5(a), 1.8(a), 1.10(a), 1.11(a), 1.14, 1.15, 1.17 (a and b), 1.23, 2.14, 2.15(b), 2.17, 2.23, 3.8, 4.6, 5.1, 5.3, 5.12, 5.14, 5.15, 5.16, 5.20, 5.21(a to d), 6.2(a and b), 6.11(a and b), 7.8, 7.14, 7.16(b)
Oxford Scientific Films: 1.2(b), 5.23
Biophotos Associates: Figure 1.4(b), 1.13, 5.24, 5.26(a to e)
Geoscience Features: 7.16(a)
John Adds: Figure 4.1
Allsport: Figure 4.10
Erica Clark: Figure 7.1

The examination questions and mark schemes on pages 110–120 appear by permission of London Examinations.

Cells and organelles

Cells, tissues and organisms

Living organisms can be distinguished from non-living things by their ability to carry out the characteristic activities of respiration, nutrition, excretion, movement, sensitivity, growth and reproduction. All living organisms are composed of basic units called **cells**. Those organisms consisting of a single cell in which all the characteristic activities take place are often described as **unicellular**, whereas those composed of many cells are described as **multicellular**.

A good example of a unicellular organism is the fungus *Saccharomyces cerevisiae*, commonly known as brewer's yeast because its activities under certain conditions result in the production of alcohol. When seen under a light microscope (Figure 1.1, top), each cell has a simple structure, consisting of a **nucleus** surrounded by **cytoplasm** enclosed by a **cell membrane**. In this organism, the living material is surrounded by a non-living **cell wall**. Within the cell, all the chemical reactions necessary to sustain life take place. New material can be added to enable growth and when the cell has reached a certain size, it will undergo reproduction, resulting in the formation of a new cell (Figure 1.1, lower photograph).

The multicellular organisms vary in their structural complexity, ranging from simple groups, or colonies, of similar cells performing the same activities to complex individuals containing thousands of specialised cells. In the simplest of the colonies, the component cells show little coordination, but as the complexity of organisms increases, so cells become specialised to carry out different functions, which contributes to the efficiency of the whole organism. Cells performing similar functions are organised into **tissues**, and the tissues contribute to the structure of the body **organs**. In mammals, for example, there are large numbers of highly specialised **liver** cells (Figure 1.2), which have the same structure and in which the same reactions take place. This liver tissue, together with other tissues, such as blood, forms the body organ we call the liver. Similarly, in flowering plants, **palisade** cells (Figure 1.2) specialised for the process of photosynthesis make up the **palisade mesophyll** tissue, which contributes to the structure of the leaf.

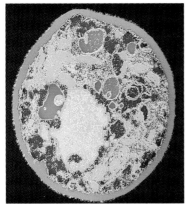

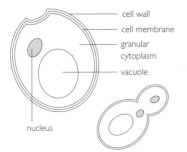

Figure 1.1 Yeast cell as seen under a light microscope; yeast cell budding

cell wall
cell membrane
granular cytoplasm
vacuole
nucleus

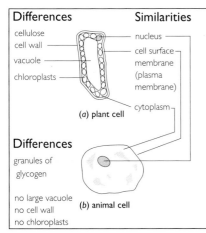

Differences
cellulose cell wall
vacuole
chloroplasts

Similarities
nucleus
cell surface membrane (plasma membrane)
cytoplasm

(a) plant cell

Differences
granules of glycogen

no large vacuole
no cell wall
no chloroplasts

(b) animal cell

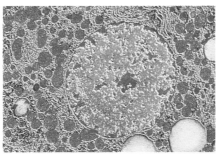 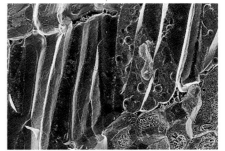

Figure 1.2 Comparison of an animal (liver) cell and a plant (leaf palisade) cell, as seen under a microscope

CELLS AND ORGANELLES

Plant and animal cells

The liver cell and the palisade cell are examples of cells specialised for different functions, but they have several features in common, as well as features that distinguish plant cells from animal cells (Figure 1.2).

Features common to both types of cell are:
- a nucleus, which contains the genetic material in the form of **chromosomes**
- the cytoplasm, containing a solution of ions and organic compounds
- the cell membrane, which forms a selective barrier between the cell and its external environment.

Plant cells have non-living **cellulose cell walls** and often contain large fluid-filled vacuoles in the cytoplasm. In addition, plant cells that photosynthesise possess green, disc-shaped structures in the cytoplasm, called **chloroplasts**. Animal cells do not possess cell walls or chloroplasts, and rarely have large vacuoles.

Cells and their organelles

Most cells are fairly small structures, ranging in size from 10μm to 150μm (0.01 to 0.15 mm) in diameter, and so far we have only considered those features of cells that are visible using the light microscope. Under the low power of the light microscope, a magnification of about 100 times is achieved, rising to about 400 times or just above at high power, depending on the lenses used. Electron microscopy (Figure 1.3) enables much greater magnification, from about 1000 to 200 000 times, and reveals the fine structure, or **ultrastructure**, of the cell. The nucleus is seen to be surrounded by a double membrane, the **nuclear envelope**, and the cytoplasm appears as a complex system of membranous sacs, the **endoplasmic reticulum**. It is possible to discover the presence and nature of other small structures, such as **mitochondria**, **ribosomes** and **Golgi apparatus**, within the cytoplasm. It is usual to refer to these structures contained within the cell as organelles. Some of them, such as mitochondria, are surrounded by membranes, while others, such as ribosomes, are not (Figures 1.4 and 1.5).

Figure 1.3 The transmission electron microscope (TEM) is able to resolve structures less than 2 nm across, 100 times better than the best light microscopes

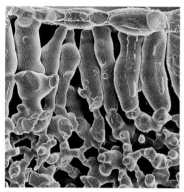

(a)

Figure 1.4 (a) Electronmicrograph of leaf palisade cell;
(b) typical plant cell structures

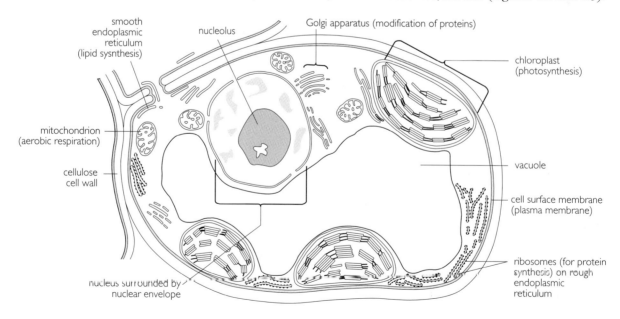

smooth endoplasmic reticulum (lipid sysnthesis)

nucleolus

Golgi apparatus (modification of proteins)

chloroplast (photosynthesis)

mitochondrion (aerobic respiration)

cellulose cell wall

vacuole

cell surface membrane (plasma membrane)

ribosomes (for protein synthesis) on rough endoplasmic reticulum

nucleus surrounded by nuclear envelope

(b)

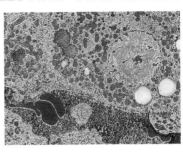

(a)

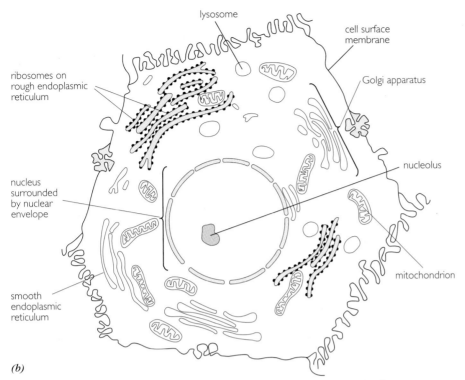

(b)

Figure 1.5 (a) Electronmicrograph of liver cell from rat; (b) typical animal cell structures

Cell surface membrane

The living material of all cells is surrounded by a cell surface membrane, sometimes referred to as the **plasma membrane**. This membrane forms a selective barrier between the cell contents and the external environment. It controls the passage of substances into and out of the cell, regulating the internal environment and providing suitable conditions for the chemical reactions that take place inside the cell. The membranes of the endoplasmic reticulum and the Golgi apparatus, together with the membranes surrounding the nucleus, appear to be similar in structure to the cell surface membrane.

Before the use of electron microscopy, the membrane was known to consist of lipid and protein molecules, but their arrangement was not known. In 1935, Davson and Danielli proposed that the membrane consists of two layers of lipid molecules, a **lipid bilayer**, coated on both surfaces with a layer of protein molecules (Figure 1.6a). They had calculated that the thickness of the membrane would be about 7.5 nm (1 nm = $1/1000\mu$m) and early electron micrographs appeared to confirm this structure.

With improvements in electron microscopes and the use of different techniques in the preparation of material to be examined, it was possible to obtain more detailed information, and in 1972 Singer and Nicolson put forward the 'fluid-mosaic' model of membrane structure (Figure 1.6b), suggesting that the membrane is a fluid structure around the cell with a mosaic of different proteins in it. This model incorporates the ideas of Davson and Danielli, and others, in that there is a lipid bilayer, but it suggests that, in addition to the protein molecules that are embedded in the bilayer, some larger protein molecules span the

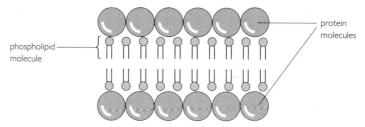

(a) Davson–Danielli model of membrane structure

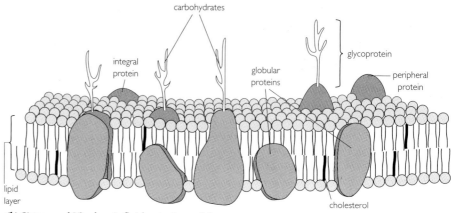

(b) Singer and Nicolson's fluid mosaic model

Figure 1.6 (a) Davson's and Danielli's 1935 model for cell surface membrane structure proposed that the lipid bilayer is coated with globular proteins; (b) Singer and Nicholson's 1972 fluid-mosaic model proposed that proteins float in the lipid bilayer

membrane. It is also suggested that the lipid and protein molecules are able to move about, accounting for the ease with which membranes fuse with each other.

As can be seen in Figure 1.6b, the cell surface membrane consists mainly of lipids and proteins. Carbohydrates are also present, but are always found in association with lipids and proteins, as glycolipids and glycoproteins respectively. The nature and general properties of these groups of molecules are discussed in chapter 2, but it is relevant here to mention some special features that are associated with the structure and properties of membranes.

Lipids

Three types of lipids are found in membranes:
- **phospholipids**, which contain a phosphate group
- **glycolipids**, which have a branching carbohydrate (polysaccharide) molecule
- **cholesterol**.

In both phospholipids and glycolipids, one part of the molecule will have an affinity, or attraction, for water (**hydrophilic**) and the other part will not mix with water (**hydrophobic**). The hydrophilic portion is said to be **polar** and the hydrophobic portion **non-polar**. In phospholipids, which are the most common lipids in the membrane, the part of the molecule containing the phosphate group is referred to as the polar head and the two fatty acid chains form the non-polar tails. In a bilayer of lipid molecules, the non-polar tails face inwards and the polar heads face outwards.

Glycolipids are less common in the membrane, but where present they always occur in the outer layer with the carbohydrate portions, forming the **glycocalyx**, extending outwards into the intercellular space. Cholesterol molecules have a different structure, but do have polar and non-polar regions. They are arranged in the bilayer with their polar groups close to the polar groups of the other lipid molecules.

Proteins

A large number of different proteins can occur in cell membranes. As shown in Figure 1.6b, some completely span the membrane (**intrinsic**), while others occur embedded in one half or located on the inner surface (**extrinsic**). Like the membrane lipids, the proteins have polar and non-polar regions. Interactions between the hydrophobic and hydrophilic regions of the proteins and the lipids help to maintain the stability of the membrane. Glycoproteins are common in membranes, the branching carbohydrate portions contributing to the glycocalyx mentioned above. As with the glycolipids, they are always found in the outer layer.

Endoplasmic reticulum

The endoplasmic reticulum (Figure 1.7) is made up of a complex system of membrane-bound flattened sacs or tubules, called **cisternae**. Where ribosomes are present on the outer surface of the membranes, it is referred to as **rough endoplasmic reticulum (RER)**, and where there are no ribosomes, it is called **smooth endoplasmic reticulum (SER)**. The cisternae of the smooth ER are usually more tubular than those of the rough ER. The **ribosomes** are involved in the synthesis of proteins, which are transported in the rough ER. The rough ER appears to be extensive in cells that actively make and secrete proteins. The smooth ER is concerned with the synthesis of lipids and is well developed in cells that produce steroid hormones and in liver cells.

Golgi apparatus

The Golgi apparatus, or Golgi body, consists of a stack of flattened cisternae and associated vesicles. It is present in all cells, but appears to be more prominent in those that are actively producing enzymes and other secretions. It is involved in the modification of proteins synthesised by the ribosomes (Figure 1.8).

Small membrane-bound cavities, or vesicles, are pinched off the endoplasmic reticulum and fuse with the cisternae of the Golgi apparatus. The vesicles from the RER contain proteins, which then have carbohydrate molecules attached to them, resulting in the formation of glycoproteins, such as are found in the cell surface membrane. Vesicles containing these modified proteins bud off from the cisternae and can be secreted from the cell. The vesicles fuse with the cell surface membrane, releasing their contents. It has been possible to trace this pathway by using radioactively labelled amino acids and following the formation of proteins, their modification to glycoproteins and subsequent release from the cell.

The Golgi apparatus has also been shown to be involved with the transport of lipids within cells and plays an important role in the formation of **lysosomes**, which are membrane-bound organelles containing digestive enzymes.

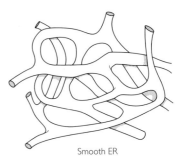

Smooth ER

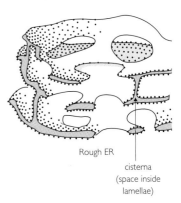

Rough ER

cisterna
(space inside
lamellae)

Figure 1.7 Endoplasmic reticulum, showing rough (RER) and smooth (SER) types

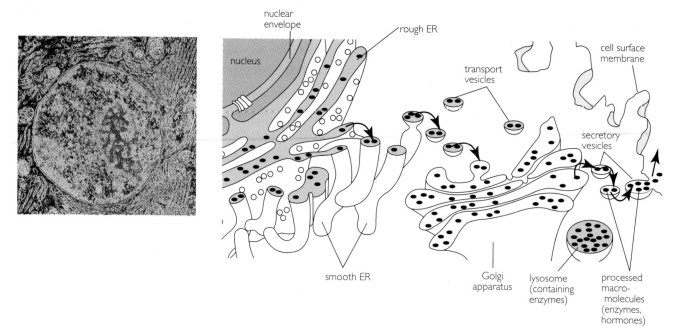

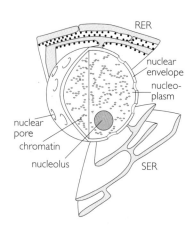

Figure 1.8 Golgi apparatus, showing its relationship with the ER and its role in packaging materials for export from a secretory cell

Lysosomes have a number of different functions within cells, including the breakdown of unwanted structures, such as old mitochondria and other worn-out organelles.

Nucleus and nuclear envelope

The nucleus of a cell is easily seen using a light microscope and appears as a dense, spherical structure within the cytoplasm, from 10 to 20 μm in diameter, surrounded by a single membrane. Electron microscopy reveals this single membrane as a double structure, forming the **nuclear envelope**, which separates the nuclear contents from the rest of the living material of the cell (Figure 1.9). The outer membrane is continuous with the membranes of the endoplasmic reticulum and bears ribosomes. The space between the two membranes is very small (from 20 to 40 nm wide) and is continuous with the cisternae of the endoplasmic reticulum. The inner and outer membranes fuse at intervals giving rise to the nuclear pores.

The nuclear envelope enables the regulation of the movement of molecules between the nucleus and the cytoplasm and helps to separate the reactions taking place in the nucleus from those taking place in the cytoplasm.

Within the nucleus is the **nucleoplasm**, a jelly-like material containing the **chromosomes** and one or more **nucleoli**. The chromosomes contain the hereditary material in the form of **DNA (deoxyribonucleic acid)** attached to proteins called **histones**, and are only visible when the nucleus is undergoing division. The nucleoli, which are not surrounded by membranes, can be seen as circular, granular structures. Their function is to make ribosomal **RNA (ribonucleic acid)** and to assemble ribosomes. During the early stages of nuclear division, the nucleoli in a cell disperse and are no longer visible, reappearing during the later stages.

Figure 1.9 Nucleus, showing internal structure and relationship with the ER

In a nucleus that is not undergoing division, the chromosomes form a diffuse network referred to as **chromatin**, so called because it stains easily with dyes and can be readily observed under the microscope.

The function of the nucleus is to control activities within the cell by controlling the chemical reactions. This is achieved by regulating the synthesis of proteins and enzymes. When a cell undergoes division, the nucleus will divide first, thus ensuring that the new cell has an exact copy of the information contained in the chromosomes.

Mitochondria

Mitochondria are barely visible under the light microscope, but electron microscopy indicates that they are rod-shaped, up to 1 μm wide and typically about 7 μm long (Figure 1.10). Each mitochondrion is surrounded by a double membrane, or envelope. The outer membrane is smooth, but the inner is folded into many shelf-like projections called **cristae** (singular: crista). The inner membrane encloses the mitochondrial **matrix**, which has a jelly-like consistency.

Mitochondria are the sites of the reactions of aerobic respiration within cells. The details of this process will be discussed in Chapter 4, but it is relevant to note here that the matrix contains enzymes involved with the **tricarboxylic acid (TCA) cycle**, alternatively known as the **Krebs cycle**, named after Sir Hans Krebs, who first discovered the sequence of reactions. The reactions in which **ATP (adenosine triphosphate)**, the energy currency of cells, is produced take place on the cristae.

Special staining techniques used on isolated fragments of the inner membrane have shown that there are structures, called **elementary particles**, on the matrix side of the cristae. These particles, which contain the enzyme involved in the synthesis of ATP, appear as tiny spheres with a diameter of about 9 nm, on stalks 4 nm high, and are spaced along the membrane at regular intervals. The elementary particles only become visible as stalked spheres when the membrane structure is disturbed, as would happen during the breaking up and preparation of mitochondria for viewing by electron microscopy.

Present in the matrix there are mitochondrial ribosomes, which are smaller than those found in the cytoplasm of the cell, and mitochondrial DNA in the form of a circular molecule.

Chloroplasts

Chloroplasts occur in the cells of the photosynthetic tissue of plants. They belong to a group of organelles known as **plastids**, which often contain pigments. Chloroplasts occur in large numbers in the palisade cells of the leaves of flowering plants. They are disc-shaped structures and appear green due to the presence of the pigment **chlorophyll**. They range from 2 to 5 μm in diameter and are 1 μm thick, easily seen using a light microscope. Electron microscopy shows that each chloroplast is surrounded by a double membrane, the **chloroplast envelope**, enclosing the stroma in which there is a system of flattened membranous sacs called **thylakoids** or **lamellae**. **Grana** are formed from several thylakoids or lamellae stacked together in the matrix (Figure 1.11).

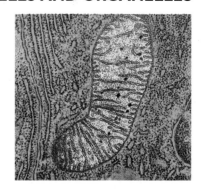

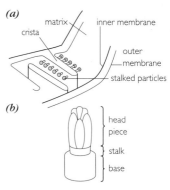

Figure 1.10 (a) Mitochondrion, showing internal structure; (b) structure of individual stalked, or elementary, particle

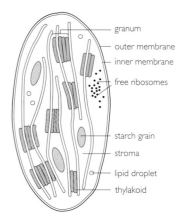

Figure 1.11 Chloroplast from leaf palisade cell, showing internal structure

The membrane system formed by the thylakoids is the place where the **light-dependent** reactions of photosynthesis occur. The chlorophyll molecules, whose function is to trap the light energy, are situated on the thylakoids. The stroma contains the enzymes necessary for the **light-independent** reactions in which carbon dioxide is converted into carbohydrates.

Also present in the stroma are small ribosomes and circular DNA molecules, starch grains and lipid droplets.

Microtubules

Microtubules are very fine, tubular organelles, which contribute to the complex network of fibrous proteins making up the **cytoskeleton** in the cytoplasm of living cells. They are straight unbranched, hollow structures, which vary in length, but have an external diameter of about 20 to 25 nm. The walls of these tubules, estimated to be about 5 nm thick, are composed of subunits of the protein **tubulin**. They can increase in length by the addition of more subunits at one end, and shorten by their removal, so they may be constantly built up and broken down within cells.

Microtubules contribute to the structure of other cell organelles, including **centrioles**, and make up the **spindle** in cells undergoing nuclear division. They are involved with the following activities within cells:
- determination and maintenance of shape
- transport of granules and vesicles within the cytoplasm
- movement of chromosomes during nuclear division.

Centrioles

Centrioles are present in most animal cells and in the cells of other organisms such as **fungi** and some **algae**. They are hollow cylindrical organelles with a diameter of 0.15 μm and length 0.5 μm. The wall of each centriole is made up of nine triplets of microtubules arranged at an angle, as shown in Figure 1.12. Where they are present in cells, they occur in pairs, arranged at right angles to each other, forming the **centrosome**. They are often situated close to the Golgi apparatus and appear to have a role in the organisation of the spindle in animal cells.

Cell walls

Cell walls surround the living contents of cells, but are themselves non-living so they are not classed as organelles. They are relatively rigid structures secreted by the living material and provide support and protection for the cell contents. In this module, we are mainly concerned with the **cellulose cell walls** of green plants, but cell walls are also present in other groups of organisms, such as the fungi, some of the **Protoctista** (algae and protozoa) and the **Prokaryotae** (bacteria).

In green plants, the first wall to be laid down following cell division is called the **primary wall** and it consists of cellulose **microfibrils** embedded in a **matrix** of complex **polysaccharide** molecules, which include **pectins** and **hemicelluloses**. Each cellulose microfibril is made up of about 2000 cellulose molecules cross-linked to each other to form a bundle. In this primary wall, the microfibrils run

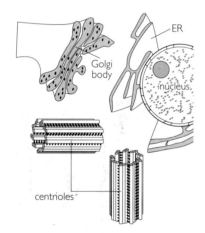

ER

Golgi body

nucleus

centrioles

Figure 1.12 Centrioles are constructed from triplets of microtubules and are associated with chromosome movements during cell division

in all directions, allowing for the growth and stretching of the wall. In most cells, after the maximum size has been reached, additional cellulose microfibrils are laid down, building up a **secondary wall** (not to be confused with **secondary thickening**, which involves the addition of new cells). The microfibrils making up each of these additional layers are usually orientated at the same angle, with each subsequent layer orientated at a slightly different angle to the one below (Figure 1.13). Palisade cells in the leaf do not normally develop secondary walls, but in other cells, such as those forming the tissue **collenchyma**, the additional layers of cellulose microfibrils can be quite thick.

The cell walls of neighbouring cells are held together by the **middle lamella**, a sticky jelly-like substance containing a mixture of **magnesium** and **calcium pectates**.

Cell walls have narrow pores through which very fine strands of cytoplasm called **plasmodesmata** (singular: **plasmodesma**) pass. The plasmodesmata range from 100 to 500 nm in diameter, providing a connection between the living contents of adjacent cells and a pathway for the movement of material from cell to cell.

The main functions of the cell wall are:
- to provide mechanical strength and support to the cell
- to resist expansion when water enters.

The cellulose microfibrils have high tensile strength, which makes the cell walls mechanically strong. The matrix contributes to the strength by improving the resistance to shearing and compression forces, as well as spreading out the microfibrils and protecting them from abrasion and chemical attack. The construction of the plant cell wall has been compared to that of reinforced concrete, where the steel rods are equivalent to the microfibrils and the concrete to the matrix.

The secondary walls of some of the cells in tissues such as **xylem**, undergo a process of **lignification**, where a complex molecule called **lignin** is deposited amongst the cellulose layers. The lignin holds the cellulose microfibrils together and makes the cell walls hard and rigid. The tissues in which lignification has occurred have extra tensile strength and a greater resistance to compression, making them ideal as construction materials. Cellulose cell walls are freely permeable to water but, where lignification occurs, the lignified areas are impermeable.

Prokaryotic and eukaryotic cells

So far, we have considered the structure and organisation of cells in which the nucleus is surrounded by a nuclear envelope, separating the genetic material from the rest of the cytoplasm, and in which there is a complex system of internal membranes and organelles. Such cells are typical of plants and animals and are termed **eukaryotic**. The cells of members of the Kingdom Prokaryotae, which includes all the bacteria, are much simpler in structure and lack complex organelles and internal membranes (Figure 1.15). They are referred to as prokaryotic and the first representatives are thought to have evolved about

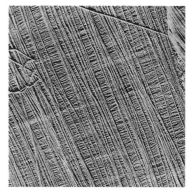

Figure 1.13 Electronmicrograph of cell wall from a plant, showing criss-crossing cellulose microfibrils (×30 000)

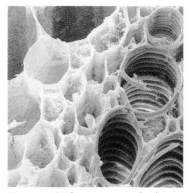

Figure 1.14 Photomicrograph of a typical xylem vessel, showing stained lignin spirals, and rings

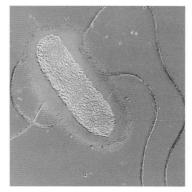

Figure 1.15 Electronmicrograph of Salmonella *food-poisoning bacterium*

3500 million years ago, whereas it has been suggested that eukaryotic cells evolved from prokaryotic ancestors 1 500 million years ago. The terms prokaryotic and eukaryotic are derived from the Greek *karyon* (meaning 'kernel' or 'nucleus'), together with the prefix *pro* (meaning 'before') and *eu* (meaning 'true'). These terms were first used in 1937 by the French marine biologist Edouard Chatton. Both prokaryotic and eukaryotic cells carry out the same activities characteristic of living organisms and so share some common features, but there are significant differences in their internal organisation.

Similarities
Both prokaryotic and eukaryotic cells have:
- a cell surface membrane
- cytoplasm
- DNA
- ribosomes.

Prokaryotic cells (Figure 1.16) and eukaryotic plant cells have cell walls, but they differ in their composition.

Differences
Most prokaryotic cells are small, usually ranging in length from 1 to 10 μm with a diameter no greater than 1 μm. The cell wall is rigid, the main component being a **peptidoglycan** called **murein** and not cellulose as in plant cell walls. Both cellulose and murein are polysaccharides, but in murein the parallel polysaccharide chains are linked by short peptides to form a complex three-dimensional network. The structure of cellulose will be discussed later. Some bacteria have a capsule or slime layer on the outside of the cell wall.

Prokaryotic cells do not have:
- a nucleus surrounded by a nuclear envelope
- mitochondria
- endoplasmic reticulum and Golgi apparatus

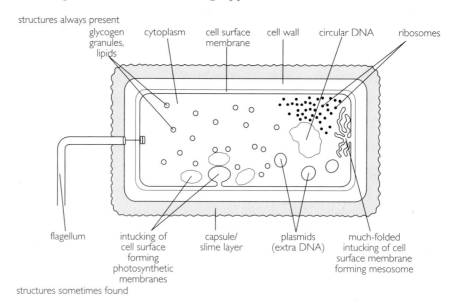

Figure 1.16 *Typical prokaryotic cell, showing structures always or sometimes present*

- chloroplasts
- a cytoskeleton of microtubules and microfilaments.

In prokaryotic cells, the DNA is arranged as a single closed loop, sometimes called a chromosome. In addition to the chromosome, there may be smaller loops of DNA, called **plasmids**, present in the cytoplasm. We have already mentioned that both types of cell have ribosomes, but those present in prokaryotes are smaller than those in eukaryotes.

Although there is no complex system of intracellular membranes, in some prokaryotes the cell surface membrane forms extensively folded regions in the cytoplasm. A good example of this is seen in the photosynthetic bacteria, where the chlorophylls and enzymes needed are found on **thylakoids** formed by intuckings (invaginations) of the cell surface membrane. Similarly, in some bacteria, the enzymes associated with aerobic respiration are located on a folded structure called the **mesosome**, again formed by invagination of the cell surface membrane. Filamentous structures called **pili**, or **fimbriae**, may be present attached to the cell wall or capsule. These can be up to 1 μm long and are usually less than 10 nm thick. **Flagella** are found in some groups of bacteria: they may be all over the cell, or limited to a group at one or both ends of the cell, or present singly. They consist of a single fibril, usually about 20 nm thick and up to several micrometres in length, rather than the 9+2 arrangement of microtubules characteristic of eukaryotes.

The differences in the structure and organisation of prokaryotic and eukaryotic cells are summarised in Table 1.1.

Table 1.1 *Table of differences between prokaryotic and eukaryotic cells.*

Prokaryotic cells	Eukaryotic cells
mostly small cells ranging in size from 1 to 10 μm	cells bigger, can be up to 400, typically 10 to 150 μm
rigid cell wall containing murein present	cell walls when present contain cellulose (green plants) or chitin (fungi)
no true nucleus	true nucleus present surrounded by nuclear envelope
circular DNA; no true chromosomes	linear DNA with associated proteins forming true chromosomes
no nucleolus	nucleolus present
no endoplasmic reticulum	endoplasmic reticulum present with associated Golgi apparatus, lysosomes and vacuoles
smaller (70S) ribosomes	larger (80S) ribosomes
no membrane-bound organelles: lack mitochondria, mesosomes in some bacteria for respiration; lack chloroplasts, photosynthetic membranes (thylakoids) in photosynthetic bacteria	many membrane-bound organelles: chloroplasts with lamellae in photosynthetic organisms; mitochondria for aerobic respiration
flagella, when present, lack microtubules	flagella have 9+2 arrangement of microtubules

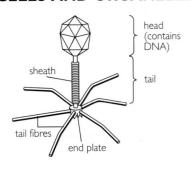

head
(contains
DNA)

sheath

tail

tail fibres

end plate

(a) Bacteriophage T₂

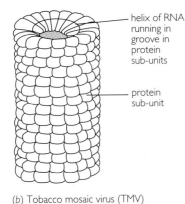

helix of RNA
running in
groove in
protein
sub-units

protein
sub-unit

(b) Tobacco mosaic virus (TMV)

Figure 1.18 Structure of
(a) bacteriophage T₂;
(b) tobacco mosaic virus

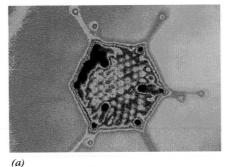

(a)

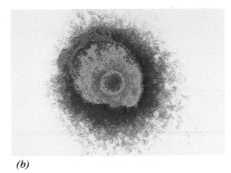

(b)

Figure 1.17 Electronmicrographs of (a) bacteriophage T2, which parasitises the gut bacterium
E. coli, *magnified; (b) tobacco mosaic virus, magnified*

Viruses as an exception to the cell theory

Viruses are much smaller than bacteria and cannot be seen using a light microscope (Figure 1.17). They range in size from about 20 nm to 400 nm and do not have a cellular structure, so they are described as **akaryotic**. They are intracellular parasites of plants, animals and bacteria, totally dependent on their host cells. The only characteristic they have in common with other living organisms is that they can reproduce once they are inside their host's cells. Viruses do not respire, feed, excrete, move, grow or respond to stimuli. They disrupt the normal activities of cells, often with harmful effects on the host organism, so they are associated with disease.

A virus consists of:
- a core of nucleic acid
- a protein coat, or capsid.

The nucleic acid may be:
- double-stranded DNA, as in *Herpes simplex*, which causes cold sores
- single-stranded DNA, as in *Parvovirus*, which causes gastroenteritis
- single-stranded RNA, as in the influenza virus and the human immuno-deficiency virus (HIV).

Most of the viruses causing diseases in plants, such as the tobacco mosaic virus, contain RNA.

The capsid surrounds the nucleic acid and consists of a number of subunits called **capsomeres**, arranged to form a geometrical structure. In addition, some viruses have an outer envelope of carbohydrate or lipoprotein and many bacteriophages (bacterial viruses) have tails that form part of the mechanism by which they gain entry to host cells (Figure 1.18a).

Movement of molecules through the cell surface membrane

In order to function efficiently, cells need to be able to take up substances from their immediate environment, to **secrete** useful substances such as **enzymes** and **hormones** manufactured within the cell and to **excrete** the waste products. For aerobic respiration to occur, oxygen and glucose are required by the cell. Carbon dioxide is produced as a waste product and has to be got rid of, or excreted, from the cell.

This movement of molecules into and out of cells involves crossing the cell surface membrane. In eukaryotic cells, the intracellular membranes of the endoplasmic reticulum and other organelles effectively divide up the cytoplasm into compartments, preventing the free movement of molecules. The cell surface membrane and the intracellular membranes are said to be **selectively**, or **partially permeable**. They have a very similar structure, so the ways in which molecules pass across these membranes is also similar. In order to understand the passage of molecules through these membranes, it is necessary to have an understanding of the fluid mosaic model of membrane structure. Due to the hydrophobic nature of the fatty acid chains of the phospholipids, it is difficult for water-soluble molecules to penetrate this barrier and so specific transport systems are required.

Materials enter and leave cells by:
- diffusion
- osmosis
- active transport
- endocytosis and exocytosis

Diffusion

The rate at which diffusion occurs depends on:
- the concentration gradient: the greater the difference in concentration between the two regions, the greater the rate
- the size of the ions or molecules: the smaller they are, the greater the rate.

Diffusion is the movement of molecules or ions from a region where they are at a high concentration to a region of lower concentration. The difference in concentration is referred to as a concentration gradient. There will be a net movement down the concentration gradient until equilibrium is reached, that is when there is a uniform distribution of the ions or molecules. The process is passive, as it does not require metabolic energy.

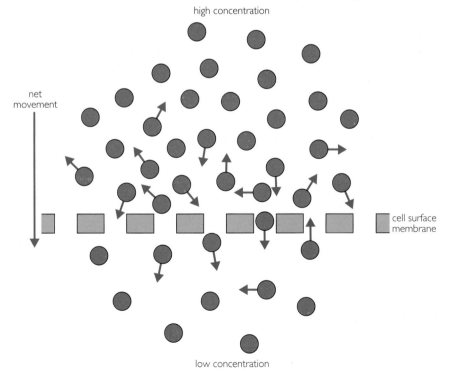

Figure 1.19 Diffusion of molecules occurs down the concentration gradient, from high to low

• the distance over which diffusion occurs: the shorter the distance, the greater the rate.

Diffusion is affected by the presence of barriers, such as the cell surface membrane and the internal membranes within cells surrounding organelles (Figure 1.19). These membranes are freely permeable to the respiratory gases oxygen and carbon dioxide, which are able to diffuse rapidly in solution depending on the concentration gradients, but are selectively permeable to other molecules. Due to the hydrophobic nature of the membranes, uncharged and lipid-soluble molecules diffuse through more readily than ions and small polar molecules such as glucose and amino acids. The polar molecules are thought to pass through membranes via channels formed by **transport**, or **channel proteins**.

Some polar molecules can diffuse across membranes more rapidly by combining with special transport proteins. An example of such a mechanism is shown by the movement of glucose molecules into cells (Figure 1.20). Transport proteins with specific binding sites for glucose are present in the cell surface membrane. Once binding with a glucose molecule has occurred, the protein changes shape and moves the glucose to the other side of the

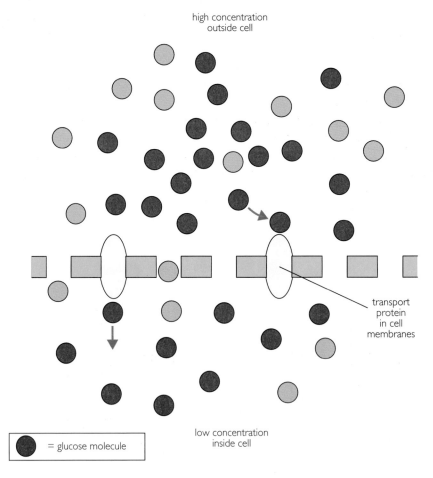

high concentration
outside cell

transport
protein
in cell
membranes

● = glucose molecule

low concentration
inside cell

Figure 1.20 Facilitated diffusion is a passive process in which certain molecules bind with membrane proteins to speed up diffusion

membrane. Once the glucose has become detached, the protein reverts to its original shape and position in the membrane, ready to pick up another glucose molecule. This process is called **facilitated diffusion**. It does not require metabolic energy and it occurs down the concentration gradient until equilibrium is reached.

The diffusion of ions across membranes is affected not only by the concentration gradient, but also by an electrical gradient. The ions will be attracted to areas of opposite charge and will move away from areas of similar charge. Their movement will be governed by a combination of concentration and electrical gradients known as an **electrochemical gradient**. The interior of most cells tends to be negatively charged, favouring the uptake of positively charged ions and repelling negatively charged ones.

Osmosis

Biological membranes are permeable to water, but there is no net movement of water into and out of cells unless **osmosis** occurs, where the movement of the water molecules is linked to the movement and concentrations of solutes on either side of the membrane.

Osmosis can be demonstrated using a simple **osmometer**, consisting of a piece of dialysis tubing containing a concentrated solution of sucrose, tied securely at both ends (Figure 1.21). The tubing is immersed in a beaker of water and left for several hours. The dialysis tubing acts as a partially permeable membrane, allowing water molecules to pass through it but preventing the movement of the sucrose molecules in the opposite direction. When it is examined later, it is seen to have increased in volume due to the entry of water molecules. A concentration gradient exists between the water in the beaker (high concentration of water molecules) and the concentrated solution of sucrose (low concentration of water molecules), so there is a net movement of water molecules into the dialysis tubing bag. Sucrose molecules can diffuse through the dialysis tubing, but because of their size they do so much more slowly than the water molecules.

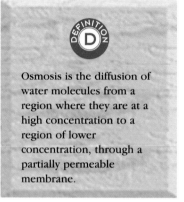

Osmosis is the diffusion of water molecules from a region where they are at a high concentration to a region of lower concentration, through a partially permeable membrane.

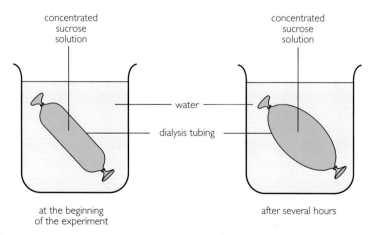

Figure 1.21 Demonstration of the osmotic movement of water through a partially permeable membrane

The topic of water relations of plant and animal cells is discussed in more detail in later texts in this series.

Active transport

Active transport involves the movement of molecules across a membrane up a concentration gradient. Ions are moved up their electrochemical gradients. This movement usually occurs in one direction and requires energy. Most active transport systems are driven by metabolic energy derived from ATP. Active transport allows cells to take up and accumulate ions and molecules necessary for metabolism as well as enabling the waste products to be removed.

The mechanisms used to move the ions or molecules across the membranes are referred to as pumps, the most widespread of which is the **sodium pump**. The majority of animal cells are able to actively pump out sodium ions against the concentration gradient. Usually, at the same time, potassium ions are actively pumped in. This combined mechanism is called a sodium-potassium pump and is important in controlling cell volume by removing sodium ions, thereby reducing the tendency of the cell to take up water by osmosis. In addition, the accumulation of potassium ions for use in cell activities, such as protein synthesis, is achieved. The **sodium-potassium pump** can also be linked to the active uptake of organic molecules, such as glucose and amino acids.

The pump is thought to consist of a protein that spans the cell membrane (Figure 1.22). On the inside of the cell sodium ions bind to special receptor sites on the protein. These ions trigger the phosphorylation of the protein, releasing energy from ATP. The protein changes shape and releases the sodium ions to the outside of the cell. Potassium ions outside the cell bind at another receptor site, causing dephosphorylation of the protein, which then changes back to its original shape, releasing the potassium ions to the inside of the cell.

There is a tendency for the sodium ions to diffuse back into the cell, down their concentration gradient, but this is a slow process because the membrane is less permeable to sodium than to potassium.

Two situations, where glucose is actively transported into cells, can be used to illustrate how the sodium-potassium pump is linked to other transport mechanisms. First, after a meal, there is a high concentration of glucose in the intestine and glucose is absorbed by diffusion down the concentration gradient. This passive process is supplemented by active uptake involving a **glucose transporter protein**, which has binding sites for both glucose molecules and sodium ions, present in the membrane of the cells lining the intestine. Second, similar membrane proteins are present in the cells lining the kidney tubules, where glucose is actively taken up against the concentration gradient from the glomerular filtrate. In both situations, the sodium-potassium pump actively transports sodium ions out of the cells against the electrochemical gradient. Glucose molecules and sodium ions bind to the glucose transporter proteins in the cell surface membranes. The sodium ions then diffuse into the cells down their electrochemical gradient, carrying the glucose molecules with them. Once inside the cells, the glucose molecules and sodium ions dissociate from the transporter protein. The glucose concentration of the cells increases, becoming

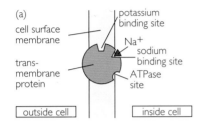

(a) cell surface membrane

trans-membrane protein

potassium binding site

Na⁺ sodium binding site

ATPase site

outside cell · inside cell

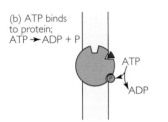

(b) ATP binds to protein; ATP → ADP + P

ATP

ADP

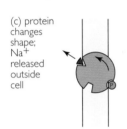

(c) protein changes shape; Na⁺ released outside cell

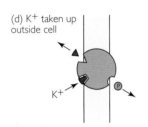

(d) K⁺ taken up outside cell

K⁺

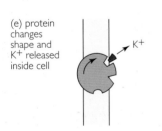

(e) protein changes shape and K⁺ released inside cell

K⁺

Figure 1.22 The sodium–potassium pump is an energy-requiring mechanism in which sodium and potassium ions are exchanged across a cell surface membrane

higher than its concentration in the blood, so glucose moves by facilitated diffusion out of the cells into the blood plasma.

Endocytosis and exocytosis

These two processes are involved with the bulk transport of materials through membranes. **Endocytosis** involves the uptake of materials into cells and **exocytosis** is the way in which materials are removed from cells. Both processes depend on the fluidity of the cell surface membrane. The molecules making up the membrane are held together by weak bonds, such as hydrogen and ionic bonds, and hydrophobic interactions, and it has been demonstrated that both the lipid molecules and the proteins can move about in the bilayer.

In endocytosis, there is an invagination of the cell surface membrane to form a vesicle around the material to be taken in, or ingested. The vesicle is pinched off and the cell surface membrane rejoins. The vesicle moves into the cytoplasm where, depending on the circumstances, other vesicles may fuse with it. Substances may be secreted from cells by the reverse of this process, in exocytosis. The vesicles move towards the cell membrane and fuse with it, releasing their contents to the exterior.

Endocytosis and exocytosis are involved when solid materials are taken up by cells (**phagocytosis**) and also when the material taken up is a liquid or a suspension (**pinocytosis**).

Phagocytosis can occur in many situations. It is the mechanism by which protozoans, such as *Amoeba*, ingest their food. The vesicles formed in *Amoeba* are referred to as **food vacuoles**. Certain white blood cells, the **neutrophils** and **monocytes**, are able to recognise foreign bacteria in the blood, engulf them and break them down within a vesicle. The food particles or invading bacteria are taken into the cells by endocytosis and, after digestion, any undigested remains are removed from the cells by exocytosis (Figure 1.24). Once the phagocytic vesicle or food vacuole has been formed, lysosomes, containing digestive enzymes, fuse with it. The contents of the lysosomes are released into the vesicle. It is important to remember that the contents of the vesicles are surrounded by a membrane, so are kept separate from the rest of the cytoplasm. Any products of the digestion of particles inside the vesicles have to diffuse through the membrane in one of the ways already described.

Pinocytosis is also widespread in both the plant and animal kingdoms. It is found in the amoeboid protozoans, white blood cells and cells in the embryo, liver and kidneys. The process is essentially similar to phagocytosis, except that liquids are taken up. Sometimes the vesicles formed are extremely small, in which case they are referred to as **micropinocytic vesicles**. These tiny vesicles are usually only detectable on electron micrographs and have been found in many different types of cells. They have been observed at the base of microvilli on the cells of the epithelium of the small intestine (Figure 1.23), where they are thought to be linked with the uptake of fat droplets.

Exocytosis of liquids is important in secretory cells. Enzymes and other products of secretory cells are formed within the endoplasmic reticulum and

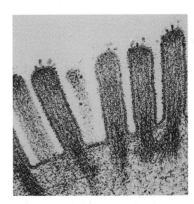

Figure 1.23 Electronmicrograph of microvilli along the edge of cells in the small intestine

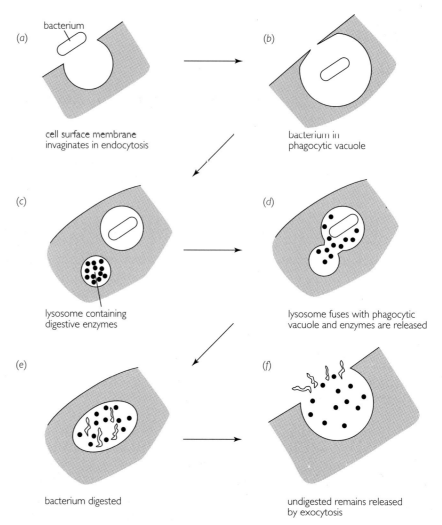

(a) bacterium

cell surface membrane
invaginates in endocytosis

(b) bacterium in
phagocytic vacuole

(c) lysosome containing
digestive enzymes

(d) lysosome fuses with phagocytic
vacuole and enzymes are released

(e) bacterium digested

(f) undigested remains released
by exocytosis

Figure 1.24 Phagocytosis of a bacterium by a neutrophil (amoeboid white blood cell), showing stages of endocytosis, intracellular digestion and exocytosis

modified in the Golgi apparatus. These substances are contained in vesicles that are budded off from the flattened cavities of the Golgi body. The vesicles then move through the cytoplasm to the cell surface, where they fuse with the membrane and exocytosis occurs, releasing the secretions.

Molecules

Role of biological molecules

In order to gain an understanding of the nature of metabolic reactions within cells, it is helpful to know something about the structure and properties of the molecules involved. Most of the groups of molecules considered here are organic and all are of great significance in the structure and functioning of living organisms.

Metabolism is the term used to describe all the reactions taking place within cells. These reactions can be divided into **anabolic**, in which compounds are being built up, or synthesised, and **catabolic**, where compounds are broken down. Anabolic reactions require energy whereas catabolic reactions often result in the release of energy.

Water

Water is necessary for life to exist on Earth. It makes up between 60 per cent and 95 per cent of the fresh mass of living organisms and is an important chemical constituent in all cells. In addition, it is also the habitat for a large number of organisms.

In order to appreciate the special properties of water molecules, it is helpful to know about their structure. In a water molecule, two **hydrogen** atoms are joined to an **oxygen** atom by covalent bonds. The oxygen atom has a nucleus, containing eight positively charged **protons** and eight **neutrons**, surrounded by eight negatively charged **electrons** (Figure 2.1). The hydrogen atom has one proton in its nucleus, plus one electron. In atoms, the electrons can be thought of as arranged in shells around the nucleus. The first, or inner, shell is the smallest and can hold up to two electrons, the second up to eight, the third up to eighteen and the fourth up to thirty-two. An atom is particularly stable when its outermost shell is full.

Atoms vary in size and do not all have four shells of electrons. The electrons in the oxygen atom are arranged in two shells: the inner shell has two and the second, outer shell has six. In each of the hydrogen atoms, there is a single electron in the first shell. The outer shell of the oxygen atom can hold up to eight electrons, so when the oxygen atom combines with the two hydrogen atoms, the electrons of the hydrogen atoms are shared with the oxygen atom, forming two **covalent bonds**. The water molecule formed is a stable molecule, but because of the arrangement of the two hydrogen atoms it has a triangular rather than a linear shape.

When covalent bonds are formed, the electrons are not always shared equally. In a water molecule, the oxygen nucleus attracts the electrons more than the hydrogen nuclei do. This results in the oxygen atom having a slight negative charge, while the hydrogen atoms have slight positive charges. This uneven charge distribution results in the molecule being polar and, because it is positive at one end and negative at the other, it is referred to as dipolar.

Figure 2.1 Atomic structures of oxygen and hydrogen, showing how they are combined in a water molecule

A hydrogen bond is a force of attraction that forms between a very electronegative atom (usually oxygen, but can be nitrogen or fluorine) and a hydrogen atom that is covalently bonded to another strongly electronegative atom. Hydrogen bonds are stronger than the dipolar force between hydrogen and oxygen, but not as strong as the covalent bond.

MOLECULES

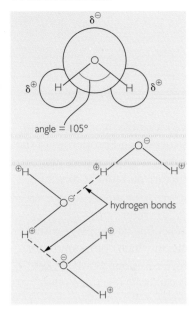

Figure 2.2 *Shape of a water molecule and formation of hydrogen bonds between electrically charged hydrogen and oxygen atoms*

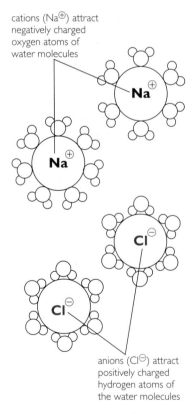

cations (Na⁺) attract negatively charged oxygen atoms of water molecules

anions (Cl⁻) attract positively charged hydrogen atoms of the water molecules

Figure 2.3 *Distribution of water molecules around sodium and chloride ions in solution*

Because water molecules are polar, they have an attraction for each other and form hydrogen bonds with neighbouring molecules (Figure 2.2).

Water as a solvent

Water is an efficient solvent for polar substances, such as salts, simple alcohols and sugars. When salts such as sodium chloride dissolve, the sodium ions and chloride ions separate and become surrounded by water molecules. The positively charged sodium ions (**cations**) are attracted to the negatively charged oxygen atoms of the water molecules and the negatively charged chloride ions (**anions**) are attracted to the positively charged hydrogen atoms (Figure 2.3).

The organic molecules such as alcohols and sugars have polar **hydroxyl** (OH) groups to which water molecules are attracted in the same way. Non-polar molecules, such as lipids, and non-polar groups on other organic molecules, do not dissolve in water.

The majority of metabolic reactions in cells take place in aqueous solution. The compounds involved are more chemically active in solution, since the molecules are able to move about more freely.

Other biologically important roles of water

Because of the very strong attraction between water molecules, giving rise to the formation of hydrogen bonds, water has a higher melting point and boiling point than other molecules of similar relative molecular mass. Methane (relative molecular mass 16), ammonia (rmm 17) and hydrogen sulphide (rmm 34) are all gases at 0 °C, but water (rmm 18) melts at 0 °C and boils at 100 °C. A great deal of energy is needed to overcome the forces of attraction between the water molecules, allowing them to move about and change from solid (ice) to liquid and from liquid to gas (water vapour). Water can be a very effective coolant, because it has a high latent heat of vaporisation. This means that it takes a great deal of heat to change the state of water from liquid to gas. When we sweat, heat energy from the body is used to evaporate the water in the sweat, cooling us down.

Water has a high specific heat capacity, indicating that it requires a lot of energy to raise the temperature of 1 kg by 1 °C. Conversely, a lot of heat energy must be lost before the temperature of the same mass of water falls by 1 °C. This property is of importance in living organisms, because it means that sudden changes in temperature, which might upset metabolic reactions in cells, are avoided. These chemical reactions are allowed to take place within a narrow temperature range, so that rates of reaction are more constant. In addition, for organisms whose habitat is water, large fluctuations in the temperature of their environment do not occur.

Water has its maximum density at 4 °C. As the temperature of a body of water, such as a pond, drops the colder water is at the surface and when it freezes, ice forms on the surface. The ice insulates the water below, enabling aquatic organisms to survive. This is especially important in cold climates and where there are cold seasons.

Water molecules are very cohesive, sticking together because of the presence of hydrogen bonds. This cohesive property is important in the transport of materials in solution within organisms. Examples are seen in the transport of ions in solution in the xylem of plants and in the transport of the soluble products of digestion in the blood plasma of animals.

Water is an important reagent in metabolic reactions, particularly in hydrolysis and as a source of hydrogen in photosynthesis.

Organic molecules

Organic molecules contain **carbon**, and in order to gain an understanding of the chemical nature of these molecules it is helpful to know a little of the structure and chemistry of the carbon atom.

The carbon atom is small with a low mass. It has six electrons arranged in two shells around the nucleus. There are two electrons in the inner shell and four in the second, outer shell. The nucleus in the centre contains six protons and six neutrons.

Because the outer shell of the carbon atom is not full, having only four electrons, it can acquire more by sharing electrons with other atoms and forming stable covalent bonds. A simple example of this is shown by the structure of methane, CH_4, where a carbon atom shares electrons with four hydrogen atoms (Figure 2.4). Each hydrogen atom has a single shell in which there is one electron, so when it combines with the carbon atom, its electron is shared with the outer shell of the carbon atom, forming a bond. In this way, the outer shell of the carbon atom acquires four shared electrons and is filled, forming a stable compound.

Covalent bonds are important in the formation and structure of organic molecules because they are strong and stable. When a carbon atom is joined to four other atoms, or groups of atoms, the four bonds are arranged spatially forming a tetrahedral shape as shown in Figure 2.5.

If you look at the formulae of most organic molecules, it is noticeable that they contain more than one carbon atom. The carbon atom is unusual in that it can bond to itself as well as to other atoms. This can result in molecules with straight chains, as seen in fatty acids, branched chains, as shown in the amino acid **alanine**, and in ring structures, such as benzene (Figure 2.6).

Carbon atoms can also form **double** or **triple** bonds, in which two or three pairs of electrons are shared. These bonds can be formed with other carbon atoms (C=C and C≡C) or with oxygen and nitrogen (C=O and C=N). Triple bonds do not often occur. In Figure 2.6, the stearic acid molecule shows an example of a C=O bond and the benzene molecule a C=C.

Carbohydrates

Carbohydrates form a large group of molecules that can be synthesised by plants. They contain carbon, together with hydrogen and oxygen. The ratio of hydrogen to oxygen atoms in the molecules is usually 2 : 1.

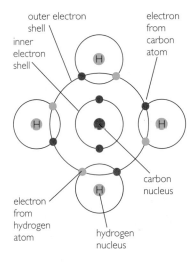

Figure 2.4 Structure of a molecule of methane gas, showing shared electrons in the orbits of the carbon and hydrogen atoms

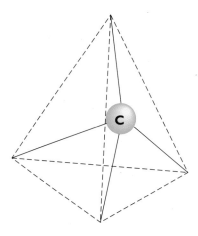

Figure 2.5 Tetrahedral arrangement of bonds around the central asymmetric carbon atom

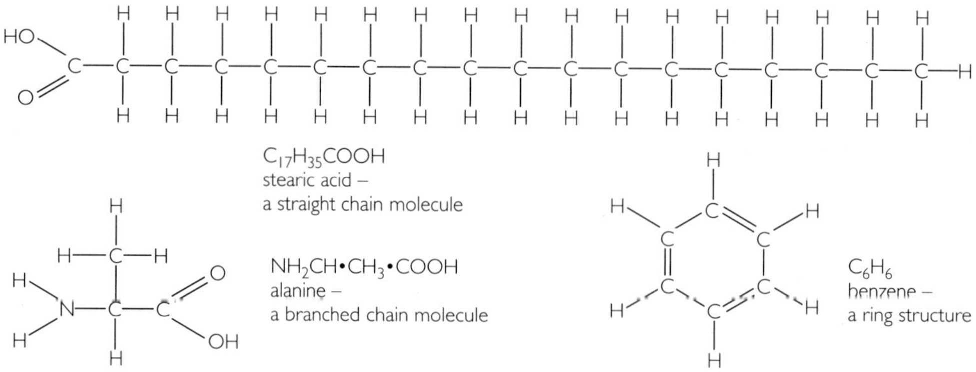

MOLECULES

Figure 2.6 Structural formulae of stearic acid, alanine and benzene to illustrate straight chains, branched chains and ring structures

Carbohydrates are common constituents of plants, making up to 90 per cent of their dry mass. The cell walls are composed of **cellulose** (a polysaccharide), energy is stored in the form of **starch** (a polysaccharide), the products of photosynthesis are transported internally as **sucrose** (a disaccharide) and the energy source for metabolism in the cells is **glucose** (a monosaccharide). Animals require carbohydrates in their diet and obtain them, either directly or indirectly, from plant sources.

Carbohydrates can be divided initially into two major groups, the sugars and the non-sugars (polysaccharides). The sugars can be further separated into simple sugars, the monosaccharides, and the compound or double sugars, the disaccharides (Table 2.1).

Monosaccharides

Monosaccharides contain carbon, hydrogen and oxygen in the ration 1 : 2 : 1, so their general formula becomes $(CH_2O)_n$, where n can be any number between 3 and 9. All monosaccharides also contain a C=O (carbonyl) group and at least

Table 2.1 *Classification and major properties of carbohydrates*

Group	Properties	Examples
monosaccharides general formula: $(CH_2O)_n$ (n = 3 to 9)	small molecules with low molecular mass; sweet tasting; crystalline; readily soluble in water	trioses, eg glyceraldehyde $(C_3H_6O_3)$; pentoses, eg ribose $(C_5H_{10}O_5)$; hexoses, eg glucose, fructose $(C_6H_{12}O_6)$
disaccharides general formula: $2[(CH_2O)_n]–H_2O$	small molecules with low molecular mass; sweet tasting; crystalline; soluble in water, but less readily than monosaccharides	sucrose, maltose, lactose; all with general formula $C_{12}H_{22}O_{11}$
polysaccharides general formula: $(C_6H_{10}O_5)_n$ (n > 300)	large molecules with high molecular mass; do not taste sweet; not crystalline; insoluble or not readily soluble in water	glycogen, starch, cellulose

22

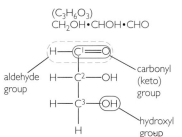

two OH (hydroxyl) groups. These two groups of atoms within the molecule are called **reactive groups** and play important roles in the reactions that take place within cells.

The simplest monosaccharides have three carbon atoms (n= 3) and are called **trioses**. An important triose, **glyceraldehyde**, is formed as an intermediate in the metabolic pathways of respiration and photosynthesis. Its structural formula is shown in Figure 2.7.

This molecule illustrates several features of carbohydrates that we have already discussed, such as:
- the ability of carbon atoms to join together to form straight chains
- the property of carbon to form covalent bonds with other atoms
- the ability of carbon to form double bonds, in this case with oxygen (C=O).

Glyceraldehyde has a carbonyl group situated at the end of the molecule at carbon–1 and two hydroxyl groups, one attached to carbon–2 and the other attached to carbon–3. It is known as an aldose, or aldo sugar, because it has an **aldehyde** group, H–C=O. Another triose, dihydroxyacetone, has the same number of carbon, hydrogen and oxygen atoms, but they are arranged differently (Figure 2.8). In this molecule, the carbonyl group is at carbon 2 and there is no hydrogen attached to it. This molecule is known as a ketose, or keto sugar, because it possesses a **ketone** group, C=O. Its structure is shown in Figure 2.8. These two compounds are isomers – they have the same molecular formula – but they have different structures due to the different linking of atoms or groups within the molecule. This form of isomerism is known as structural isomerism and is common in the carbohydrates.

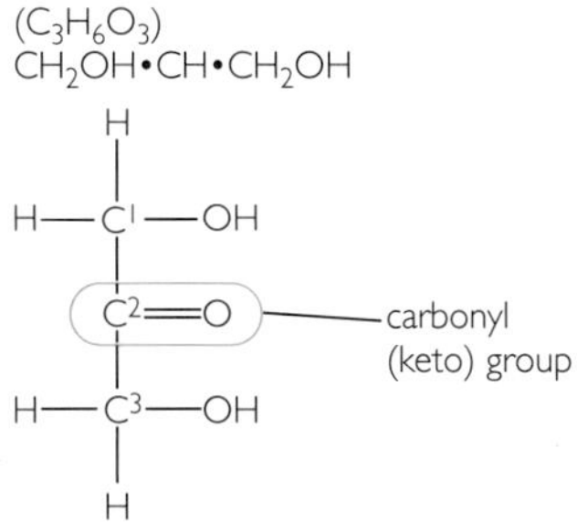

All the sugars that occur naturally are derived from trioses. All the aldoses are formed from glyceraldehyde and all the ketoses from dihydroxyacetone.

Pentoses are monosaccharides with five carbon atoms in the molecule and the general formula $C_5H_{10}O_5$. Like trioses, the pentoses have a carbonyl group and at least two hydroxyl groups. **Ribose**, an important constituent of **RNA** (**ribonucleic acid**), is an aldose and can exist as a chain or in a ring form (Figure 2.9).

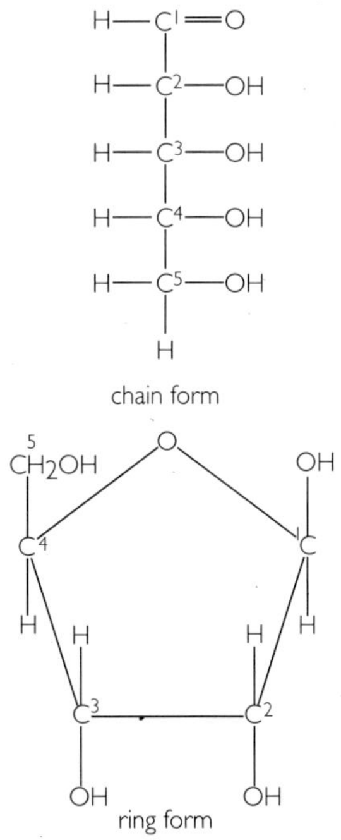

Hexoses are the six carbon sugars, all having the general formula $C_6H_{12}O_6$. They can exist as straight chains or as rings. When a ring forms, the carbonyl group reacts with one of the hydroxyl groups in the chain. The straight chain and ring forms of two common hexoses, **glucose** and **fructose**, are shown in Figure 2.10.

In glucose, a six-membered ring is formed from five carbon atoms and an oxygen atom. This type of structure is called a **pyranose** ring. Fructose forms a five-membered ring, with four carbon atoms and one oxygen atom, called a **furanose** ring. The six-atom ring form is the more stable ring form for the aldoses (glucose and galactose) and the five-atom ring for the ketoses such as fructose. The ring forms are the more usual forms for both the pentoses and hexoses and it is as such that they are incorporated into disaccharides and polysaccharides.

Figure 2.7 Structural formula of glyceraldehyde (compare with Figure 2.8)

Figure 2.8 Structural formula of dihydroxyacetone (compare with Figure 2.7)

Figure 2.9 Structural formula of 5-carbon sugar ribose, showing chain and ring forms

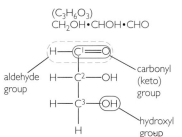

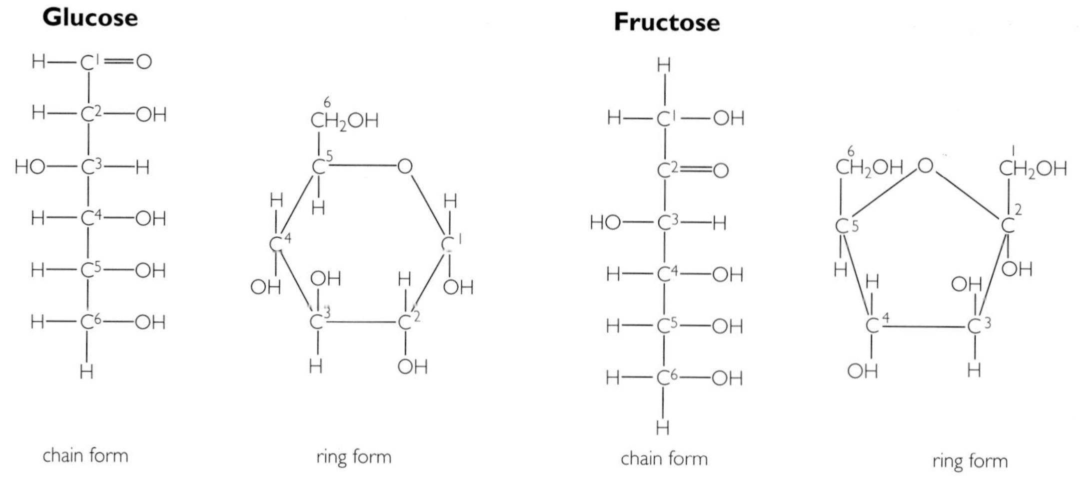

MOLECULES

Glucose

chain form

ring form

Fructose

chain form

ring form

Figure 2.10 Structural formulae of 6-carbon sugars glucose and fructose, showing chain and ring forms

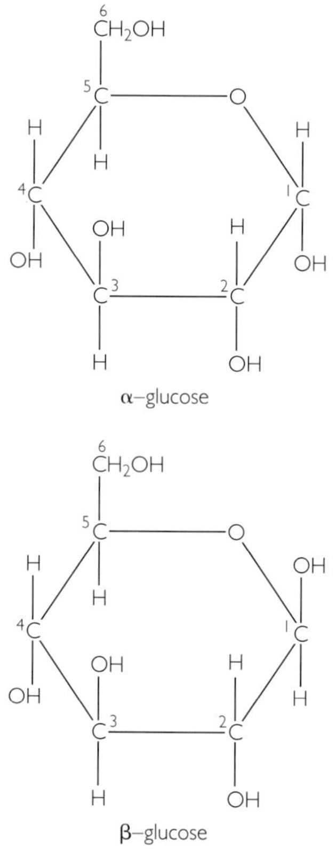

α–glucose

β–glucose

Figure 2.11 Structural formulae of α- and β-glucose, showing stereoisomerism

Glucose can exist in two different ring forms: one where the hydroxyl group on carbon 1 is below the ring (*α*-**glucose**) and one where the hydroxyl group is above the ring (*β*-**glucose**) (Figure 2.11). These are known as *α*- and *β*- isomers and, because the atoms and groups are arranged differently in space, are examples of **stereoisomerism**. The existence of these two isomers leads to a greater variety in the formation and the properties of polymers. Starch is a polymer of *α*-glucose and cellulose is a polymer of *β*-glucose.

Disaccharides

When two monosaccharide molecules undergo a condensation reaction, a disaccharide molecule is formed and a molecule of water is removed. The bond formed between the two monosaccharide **residues**, as they are now called, is a **glycosidic bond**. In the example shown in Figure 2.12, two glucose molecules are shown combining to form a molecule of maltose, with the removal of water. Because the bond is formed between the groups attached to carbon 1 of the first glucose molecule and carbon 4 of the second glucose molecule, it is referred to as a 1,4 glycosidic bond.

The formation of sucrose involves a condensation reaction between glucose and fructose. In this case, the groups on different carbon atoms are involved and a 1,2 glycosidic bond is formed (Table 2.2).

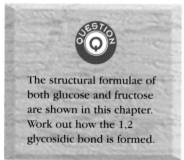

The structural formulae of both glucose and fructose are shown in this chapter. Work out how the 1,2 glycosidic bond is formed.

$C_6H_{12}O_6$ glucose + $C_6H_{12}O_6$ glucose ⇌ $C_{12}H_{22}O_{11}$ maltose + H_2O water

1,4 glycosidic bond formed

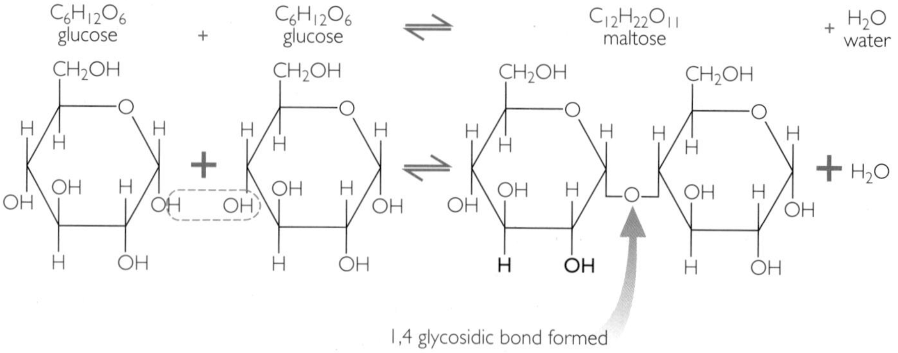

Figure 2.12 Formation of 1,4 glycosidic bond by condensation of two molecules of glucose

Table 2.2 *Characteristics of the commonly occurring disaccharides*

Disaccharide	Constituent monosaccharides	Type of glycosidic bond	Occurrence and importance
lactose	glucose galactose	1,4	present in mammalian milk, so important in diet of infants
maltose	glucose	1,4	formed by action of amylase (enzyme) on starch during digestion in animals and during germination of seeds
sucrose	glucose fructose	1,2	found in sugar cane and sugar beet; form in which sugars are transported in plants; storage compound in some plants, eg onions

On hydrolysis, which requires water to be present, disaccharides can be split into their constituent monosaccharides. Within cells, these reactions are catalysed by specific enzymes. In the laboratory, it is possible to hydrolyse disaccharides by heating in solution with acids.

All the monosaccharides are described as **reducing sugars**. When solutions of these sugars are heated with Benedict's reagent (an alkaline solution of blue copper sulphate [$CuSO_4$]), a red-brown precipitate of insoluble copper oxide [Cu_2O] is formed. The aldehyde groups of aldoses, such as glucose and galactose, are able to reduce the copper(II) in the copper sulphate to copper(I) in copper oxide. As a result, the aldehyde groups are oxidised to **carboxyl (COOH)** groups. In sugars that do not have aldehyde groups, such as the ketoses, the carbonyl group on carbon–2 changes place with the hydroxyl group on carbon–1, so they can also reduce copper(II) to copper(I) when heated with the reagent.

In some disaccharides, for example maltose and lactose, an aldehyde group is available, so a positive result is obtained when these sugars are tested. When sucrose is heated with the reagent, no colour change occurs, as the aldehyde groups are not available. Sucrose is described as a non-reducing sugar. If a solution of sucrose is boiled with dilute hydrochloric acid, cooled, neutralised and retested with the reagent, the familiar brown-red precipitate develops, because the sucrose has been hydrolysed into its constituent monosaccharides, glucose and fructose.

Polysaccharides

Polysaccharides are **macromolecules**, with very large relative molecular masses ranging from 5000 to 10 000. They are also **polymers** formed from large numbers of monosaccharide **monomers**, joined together by covalent bonds by a process known as **condensation polymerisation**. This process is essentially similar to the way in which two monosaccharides are joined to form a disaccharide, which has already been described.

Table 2.3 *Summary of features of some common polysaccharides*

Polysaccharide	Monomer	Type of glycosidic bond	Shape of molecule
starch	α–glucose (amylose)	1,4	unbranched chain wound into a helix
starch	α–glucose (amylopectin)	1,4 with some 1,6	tightly packed branched chain
glycogen	α–glucose	1,4 with more 1,6 than amylopectin	very branched compact molecule
cellulose	β–glucose	1,4	unbranched straight chains

The commonly occurring polysaccharides starch, glycogen and cellulose are all polymers of glucose. The glucose monomers are linked together by glycosidic bonds. The different nature of these polysaccharides depends on the isomer of glucose involved and on the type of glycosidic bond (Table 2.3).

Starch

Starch is a polymer of α-glucose monomers and is a mixture of amylose and amylopectin (Figure 2.13). Amylose makes up about 30 per cent of starch and consists of unbranched chains in which the monomers are joined by 1,4 glycosidic bonds. The molecules usually contain more than 300 glucose monomers and adopt a helical shape. The coils have six monomers per turn and are held together by hydrogen bonds formed between the groups attached to the carbon atoms. When iodine in potassium iodide solution is used to detect the presence of starch, a complex forms with the glucose monomers in the amylose helix. This leads to the formation of the characteristic blue-black colour. Amylopectin, which constitutes the remaining 70 per cent of starch,

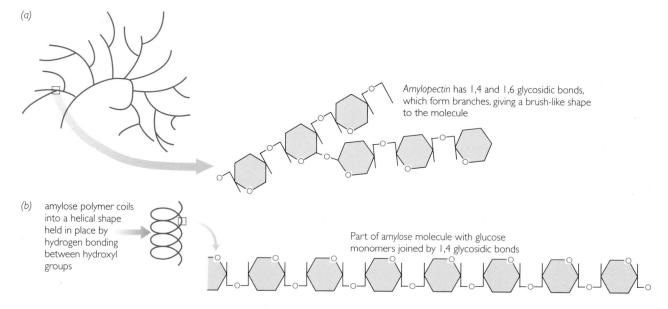

(a)

Amylopectin has 1,4 and 1,6 glycosidic bonds, which form branches, giving a brush-like shape to the molecule

(b) amylose polymer coils into a helical shape held in place by hydrogen bonding between hydroxyl groups

Part of *amylose* molecule with glucose monomers joined by 1,4 glycosidic bonds

Figure 2.13 Structure of (a) amylopectin and (b) amylose to illustrate how 1,4 and 1,6 glycosidic bonds affect three-dimensional shape of polysaccharide

consists of chains of glucose monomers linked with 1,4 glycosidic bonds. Branches arise from these chains due to the formation of 1,6 bonds at various points, about every 20 to 30 residues along their length. The resulting molecule, consisting of several thousand monomers, is much branched and also coiled into a compact shape.

Starch functions as an important storage molecule in plants. It is particularly well suited to this function because:
- it is compact and does not take up much space
- it is insoluble so it cannot move out of the cells in which it is stored
- it has no osmotic effects
- it does not become involved in chemical reactions in the cells
- it is easily hydrolysed to soluble sugars by enzyme action when required.

Starch molecules are built up into starch grains inside special structures called **amyloplasts**, which are present in the cytoplasm of plant cells. Starch grains may also be built up in the stroma of chloroplasts. The starch molecules appear to be deposited in concentric layers around a central point, forming the grains, which have characteristic shapes according to the species (Figure 2.14).

Figure 2.14 Photomicrograph of starch grains from a potato

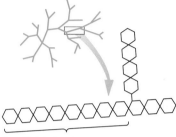

8 to 10 1,4 glycosidic links between 1,6 branch points

(a)

Glycogen

Glycogen is also a polymer of α-glucose monomers in which there are both 1,4 and 1,6 glycosidic bonds (Figure 2.15a). It is very similar to amylopectin in that it is branched, but the branch points occur more frequently, every 8 to 12 residues, forming a very compact structure. Glycogen is an energy storage molecule in animals, where it occurs in the liver cells and in muscle tissue (Figure 2.15b). It is also found in the cytoplasm of bacterial cells. As with amylose and amylopectin in starch, glycogen is well suited to its function, taking up little space and preventing too high a concentration of glucose in the cells. It can be readily hydrolysed to glucose for use as a respiratory substrate when required.

Cellulose

Cellulose is a polymer of β-glucose monomers joined by 1,4 glycosidic bonds to form straight unbranched chains (Figure 2.16). Due to the orientation of the monomers, there is no tendency for the molecules to coil into a helical shape. Each chain contains thousands of β-glucose residues with hydroxyl groups projecting out all round. Hydrogen bonding occurs between the hydroxyl groups on adjacent chains forming cross links that hold the chains together. Up to 2000 such chains can be held together to form a **microfibril**, which can be many micrometres in length. Microfibrils have great tensile strength, enabling them to resist pulling forces.

Cellulose is an important structural component of plant cell walls, where its tensile strength is important. The cellulose microfibrils are embedded in a kind of 'cement', or **matrix**, which holds them together. The matrix consists of a mixture of pectins and hemicelluloses, which will be discussed later. Cellulose can be hydrolysed in the laboratory only by treatment with concentrated acids. Despite the abundance of cellulose, there are relatively few groups of living organisms capable of producing the enzyme **cellulase**, which catalyses the digestion of cellulose to glucose. Some prokaryotes and fungi are

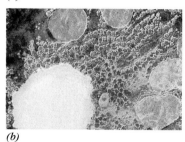

(b)

Figure 2.15 (a) Structure of glycogen to illustrate a branched polysaccharide of animal origin; (b) electronmicrograph of glycogen granules in cytoplasm of liver cell, showing association with ER (× 12 000)

MOLECULES

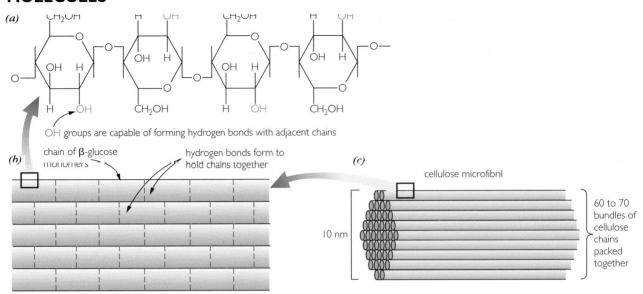

Figure 2.16 Structure of cellulose, illustrating that cellulose microfibrils (c) consist of hydrogen-bonded chains (b) of β-glucose monomers (a)

able to synthesise the enzyme, but the ruminant mammals, for whom cellulose is such an important food source, depend on large populations of symbiotic bacteria in their guts to break down the cellulose for them. These mammals can then absorb the nutrients released by the bacteria.

Other polysaccharides

Other polysaccharides and some closely related compounds are of biological significance and any survey of the carbohydrates would be incomplete without reference to them.

- **Callose** is another polymer of glucose found in plants. The monomers are linked by 1,3 glycosidic bonds. Callose is found lining the pores of the sieve plates in phloem sieve tubes and should not be confused with callus, a type of parenchyma tissue often produced near the surface of a wound or in the formation of a union between the scion and the stock in grafting.
- **Inulin** is a polymer of fructose, found as a storage carbohydrate in some groups of plants, for example *Dahlia* tubers.
- **Pectins** and hemicelluloses are associated with the cellulose cell walls in plants. Pectins are polysaccharides formed from galactose and its associated organic acid. The chains have negative charges and attract calcium (Ca^{2+}) ions forming calcium pectate, which attracts and holds water molecules forming a gel. This gel makes up the matrix of the cell wall in which the cellulose microfibrils are embedded. Hemicelluloses are very similar in composition to cellulose in that they consist of short chains of β-glucose residues linked by 1,4 glycosidic bonds, but they have in addition side branches of other sugars, such as galactose. The hemicellulose molecules are held tightly by hydrogen bonds to the cellulose microfibrils in the cell wall and also to the pectate molecules, thus linking the pectate and the cellulose.
- **Chitin** has a structure very similar to cellulose, in that bundles of long parallel chains are formed. Each chain is composed of β-glucose residues

Figure 2.17 Tropical stag beetle exoskeleton, composed of chitin, a hard polymer of amino sugars

linked by 1,4 glycosidic bonds, but the hydroxyl group at carbon–2 of the β-glucose has been replaced by NH.CO.CH$_3$. These residues are often referred to as amino sugars. Chitin occurs in the walls of fungal hyphae and forms the exoskeleton in arthropods (Figure 2.17).

- **Murein** is a polysaccharide present in the cell walls of prokaryotes, where the chains are composed of the same amino sugar found in chitin molecules, together with another similar amino sugar. These two alternate along the chain. Adjacent chains are cross-linked by amino acids.
- **Mucopolysaccharides**, found in bone, cartilage and synovial fluid, are polymers of organic acids derived from sugars and amino acids.

Lipids

Lipids are **fats** and **oils**, organic compounds containing carbon, hydrogen and oxygen. The same three elements are involved in the structure of carbohydrates, but the amount of oxygen in the molecule is much less than in the carbohydrates. Lipids are insoluble in water, but soluble in organic solvents such as acetone and ether. They are relatively small molecules compared to the polysaccharides, but because they are insoluble they tend to join together to form globules.

The naturally occurring fats and oils are esters formed by condensation reactions between glycerol (an alcohol) and organic acids known as **fatty acids**. During formation, three molecules of water are removed.

$$\text{glycerol} \quad + \quad \text{fatty acid} \quad \rightleftharpoons \quad \text{ester + water}$$
$$\text{(an alcohol)} \quad \text{(organic acid)}$$

Glycerol, with the formula C$_3$H$_8$O$_3$, has three **hydroxyl (OH)** groups, all of which can take part in condensation reactions with a fatty acid. The resulting ester is called a triglyceride (or triacylglycerol) (Figure 2.18).

Fatty acid molecules are much larger than glycerol molecules and consist of long, non-polar hydrocarbon chains with a polar, carboxyl group (COOH) at one end. There are many different fatty acids present in living organisms, but they can be divided into saturated fatty acids, which possess only single bonds in their hydrocarbon chains, and unsaturated fatty acids, which have one or more double bonds. Lipids composed of saturated fatty acids are termed saturated fats and those built up of unsaturated fatty acids are unsaturated fats. In order to appreciate the differences between the two, let us compare the structure of stearic acid, with a formula of C$_{17}$H$_{35}$COOH, with oleic acid, C$_{17}$H$_{33}$COOH (Figure 2.19). Without looking at the arrangement of the atoms within the molecules, it can be seen that oleic acid has two fewer hydrogen atoms than stearic.

Fatty acids play an important role in cells. They can be broken down and oxidised to release energy for cell metabolism or built up into triglycerides, forming an energy store. Fatty acids can also be converted to phospholipids, which are important constituents of cell membranes.

Triglycerides are the commonest lipids in living organisms and their primary importance is as energy stores. They are compact and insoluble and can be

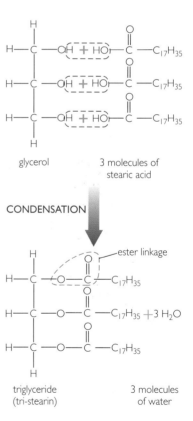

Figure 2.18 Formation of a triglyceride by condensation of three molecules of fatty acid with a molecule of glycerol

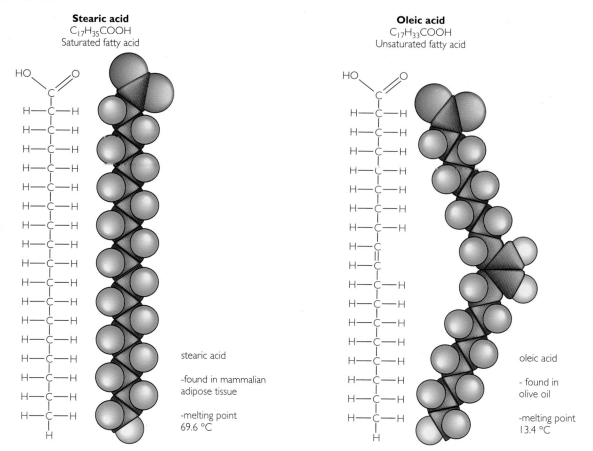

Stearic acid
C₁₇H₃₅COOH
Saturated fatty acid

stearic acid

-found in mammalian
adipose tissue

-melting point
69.6 °C

Oleic acid
C₁₇H₃₃COOH
Unsaturated fatty acid

oleic acid

- found in
olive oil

-melting point
13.4 °C

Figure 2.19 Comparison of structure and properties of a saturated fatty acid (stearic acid) and an unsaturated fatty acid (oleic acid) the right-hand section of each diagram shows a molecular model of the substance

stored at high concentrations in cells, where they occur as small droplets suspended in the cytoplasm. They release approximately twice as much energy per gram as carbohydrates, but the process of energy release requires oxygen. In addition, more water is released on oxidation than from the oxidation of carbohydrates. This is known as metabolic water and is important to organisms living in dry climates. Oils are the major food store in many seeds (sunflower, rape) and fruits (palm, olive). In animals, fats are stored in **adipose** tissue, which consists of large fat cells found below the skin and around the body organs. In addition to providing an energy store, the fatty tissues protect vital organs, provide insulation and, in aquatic animals, buoyancy.

Phospholipids

Phospholipids are similar to lipids in that they are esters of fatty acids and glycerol, but one of the fatty acid chains is replaced by a polar group associated with a phosphate molecule (Figure 2.20). The polar group is very soluble in water, whereas the non-polar hydrocarbon chains of the fatty acids are not. At an air–water, or oil–water interface, the phospholipid molecules orientate themselves so that their polar heads are in the water. Phospholipids are important constituents of cell membranes and their involvement is described in Chapter 1.

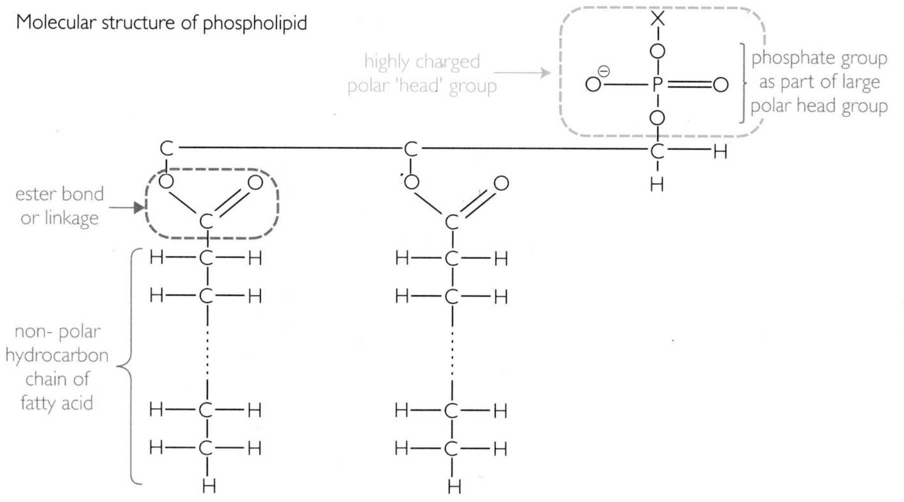

Molecular structure of phospholipid

highly charged polar 'head' group →

phosphate group as part of large polar head group

ester bond or linkage →

non-polar hydrocarbon chain of fatty acid

Figure 2.20 *Structure of a phospholipid molecule, illustrating how its polar nature derives from a highly charged phosphate group (and other associated groups) at the 'head' of the molecule*

Proteins

Proteins are complex organic molecules containing carbon, hydrogen, oxygen and nitrogen. Sometimes they contain sulphur and may form complexes with other molecules containing phosphorus, iron, zinc and copper. Proteins are macromolecules, with relative molecular masses between 10^4 and 10^6, consisting of one or more unbranched **polypeptide** chains built up from **amino acid** monomers linked by **peptide bonds**.

Each protein has a characteristic three-dimensional shape resulting from the coiling and folding of the constituent polypeptide. When considering the structure of a protein, it is usual to describe three or four different levels of organisation of the molecule. These levels are often referred to as the primary, secondary, tertiary and quaternary structures.

The **primary structure** of a protein is the number, type and sequence of the amino acids that make up the polypeptide chain. The primary structure is specific to each protein and coded for by the DNA of the cell in which the protein is made. As the amino acids are fundamental to the structure of proteins, it is worth considering their structure and properties and the way in which they are bonded together.

Amino acids are crystalline solids and are soluble in water. They have the general formula $NH_2.RCH.COOH$, where R varies from a single hydrogen atom to more complex groups, including ring structures. They contain an amino or amine (NH_2) group at one end of the molecule and a carboxylic (COOH) group at the other end. There are twenty common amino acids found in living organisms.

The amino group has basic properties and the carboxyl group has acidic properties. Compounds with both basic and acidic properties are called **amphoteric**. In living cells, the pH is usually neutral, so both the groups become ionised, leaving the molecule with a positive charge at one end and negatively charged at the other (Figure 2.21). This type of molecule is sometimes referred to as a zwitterion, or double ion.

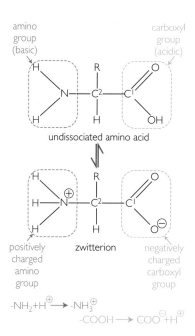

amino group (basic)

carboxyl group (acidic)

undissociated amino acid

positively charged amino group

zwitterion

negatively charged carboxyl group

$-NH_2 + H^{\oplus} \longrightarrow -NH_3^{\oplus}$
$-COOH \longrightarrow COO^{\ominus} + H^{\oplus}$

Figure 2.21 *Structure of undissociated and ionised (zwitterion) forms of an amino acid, to show basic and acidic properties*

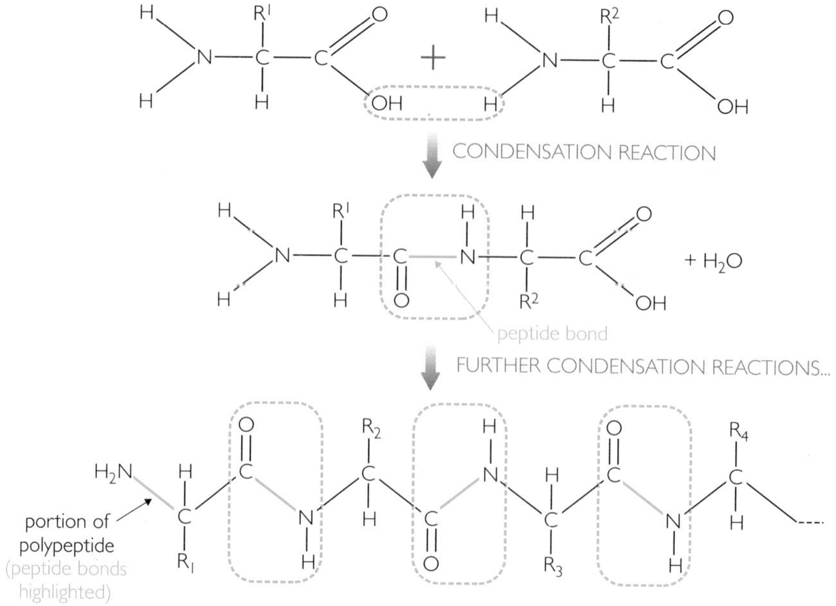

Figure 2.22 *Formation of a peptide bond by condensation of two amino acid molecules, and further condensation to generate a polypeptide*

Two amino acids can join together in a condensation reaction to form a **dipeptide**. The bond formed between the two is called a peptide bond and a molecule of water is removed. Further condensation reactions enable additional amino acids to be added, resulting in a polypeptide chain (Figure 2.22).

The most important role of amino acids in cells is as the monomers involved in protein synthesis. Green plants are able to synthesise all the amino acids they require from the products of photosynthesis and nitrate ions absorbed from the soil. Animals can synthesise some of the amino acids they require, but need to obtain the rest from their diet. We need to obtain eight amino acids from our diet. These are known as the **essential** amino acids, and we are able to synthesise all the rest that we require to make the proteins we need. Amino acids are also involved in the synthesis of other compounds, such as nucleic acids and cytochromes.

In protein molecules, polypeptide chains are either coiled into a spiral spring, the α-**helix** or linked together to form β-**pleated** sheets. Both these arrangements of the chains constitute the secondary structure of the protein. These are stable structures, maintained by hydrogen bonding between different groups on the amino acid residues of the chains.

In an α-helix, the coils in the polypeptide chain are held in place by hydrogen bonds that form between the hydrogen atoms of the NH group of one amino acid and the oxygen atom of the CO group of another amino acid further along the chain. It has been estimated that the α-helix makes one complete turn every 3.6 amino acid residues. In the fibrous protein keratin, which is found in hair, nails and skin (Figure 2.23), several α-helices are held together by bonds formed between adjacent chains and this protein does not have a tertiary structure. The bonds, in this case disulphide bridges, form cross-links and the bundles of molecules have strength and the ability to stretch (Figure 2.24a).

Figure 2.23 *Rhino horn is composed of keratin, a tough fibrous protein consisting of alpha-helices bonded together in a mineral matrix*

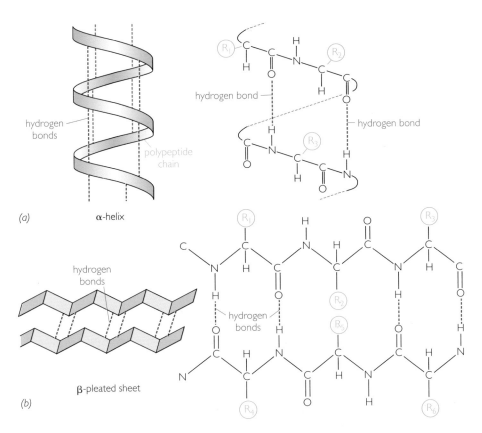

Figure 2.24 Comparison between the arrangement of the amino acids in (a) an alpha-helix and (b) a beta-pleated sheet, illustrating the role of hydrogen bonding in secondary protein structure

In a β-pleated sheet, hydrogen bond formation takes place between the CO and NH groups of the amino acid residues of one chain and the NH and CO groups of neighbouring chains. This arrangement, giving the protein a high tensile strength, is found in silk fibroin, produced by silkworms. The fibroin cannot be stretched, but it is very supple.

The fibrous protein **collagen**, present in connective tissues such as bone and tendons, is made up of three polypeptide chains coiled round each other, forming a triple helix. It cannot be stretched, but is flexible (Figure 2.24b).

In most proteins there are regions of α-helix and regions of β-pleating, but the folding of the polypeptide chain into a compact, globular shape is referred to as the **tertiary structure**. The bending and folding is irregular and it is the result of the formation of different types of bonds between the amino acid residues.

The nature of the R-groups of the constituent amino acids and their interactions play an important role in determining and maintaining the specific shape of a protein molecule. Some of the R-groups will be polar and attracted to water, whilst others are non-polar. The polar groups are referred to as **hydrophilic**, or 'water-loving', and the non-polar groups are **hydrophobic**, or 'water-hating'. Folding of the polypeptide chain results in a structure with most of the hydrophilic groups on the outside of the molecule and the hydrophobic groups on the inside. This arrangement is more stable, particularly for globular proteins in living cells.

hydrogen bonding

disulphide bonding

ionic bond

Figure 2.25 Types of bonding commonly found in the tertiary structure of proteins

Four polypeptide chains make up the haemoglobin molecule. Each chain contains 574 amino acids.

β   β

α   α

Each chain is attached to haem group that can combine with oxygen.

Figure 2.26 Structure of a molecule of haemoglobin, showing how the alpha and beta chains associate around the iron-containing haem groups in the quaternary structure of a globular protein

Some of the R-groups can form:
- hydrogen bonds between their hydrogen and oxygen atoms and those of other R-groups
- ionic bonds
- disulphide bridges (applies to sulphur-containing amino acid residues).

The different types of bonds are illustrated in Figure 2.25.

Complex proteins may consist of more than one polypeptide chain and so are described as having a **quaternary structure**. The polypeptide chains in complex proteins may be all of one type or of different types. In haemoglobin, a protein present in the blood, there are four polypeptide chains held together by bonds of the types described above. Two of the chains, the α-globin chains, each contain 141 amino acid residues, and the other two, the β-globin chains, contain 146 amino acid residues. Each chain is associated with an iron-containing haem group. The structure of haemoglobin was worked out by Kendrew and Perutz (Figure 2.26).

Proteins are abundant in living organisms, but because of their diverse nature it is difficult to produce a simple classification. It is customary to group them either according to their structure (Table 2.4) or to their functions (Table 2.5) within living organisms.

Table 2.4 *Classification of proteins according to their structure*

Fibrous	Globular
secondary structure important; consist mainly of α-helix or β-pleated sheets	tertiary structure important; bent and folded into spherical shapes
insoluble in water	soluble in water
structural functions eg keratin, collagen	enzymes, antibodies, hormones eg amylase, globulins, insulin

Table 2.5 *Classification of proteins according to their function*

Function	Example	Location
contraction	myosin, actin	muscle tissue
enzymes	amylase	endosperm of starchy seeds; human duodenum
hormones	insulin	present in blood; secreted from islets of Langerhans in pancreas
homeostasis	soluble proteins	can act as buffers, stabilising pH in body cells
protection	antibodies fibrinogen	produced by lymphocytes in the blood present in blood as part of blood clotting mechanism
storage	aleurone layer	in seeds
structure	collagen keratin	skin hair
transport	haemoglobin	transport of oxygen in vertebrate blood

Under certain circumstances, the three-dimensional shape of a globular protein molecule can change. This change may be temporary or permanent, affecting the tertiary structure of the protein, but not altering its primary structure. Alteration of the tertiary structure affects the biological role of the protein, especially in the case of enzymes, which depend on the specific configuration of the active site in order to form an enzyme–substrate complex. This loss of shape is referred to as **denaturation** and can be caused by an increase in temperature, a change in pH, high concentrations of salts, the presence of ions of heavy metals and organic solvents.

Nucleic acids

Nucleic acids are macromolecules with relative molecular masses ranging from 10^4 to 10^6. They are built up of nucleotide subunits, which join together forming long unbranched chains. The bonds that link the subunits together are sugar–phosphate bonds, sometimes referred to as phosphodiester bonds. A nucleotide is made up of:
- a pentose (5–carbon sugar)
- an organic nitrogenous base
- phosphoric acid.

A condensation reaction between the pentose and the base results in the formation of a **nucleoside**, with the removal of a molecule of water. A further condensation reaction between the nucleoside and phosphoric acid produces a nucleotide. A **phosphoester** linkage is formed and another molecule of water is eliminated (Figure 2.27).

A range of nucleotides can be found in living cells, differing in their pentose and organic bases. Two pentoses, ribose and deoxyribose, are involved. These sugars differ in that deoxyribose ($C_5H_{10}O_4$) has one fewer oxygen atoms than

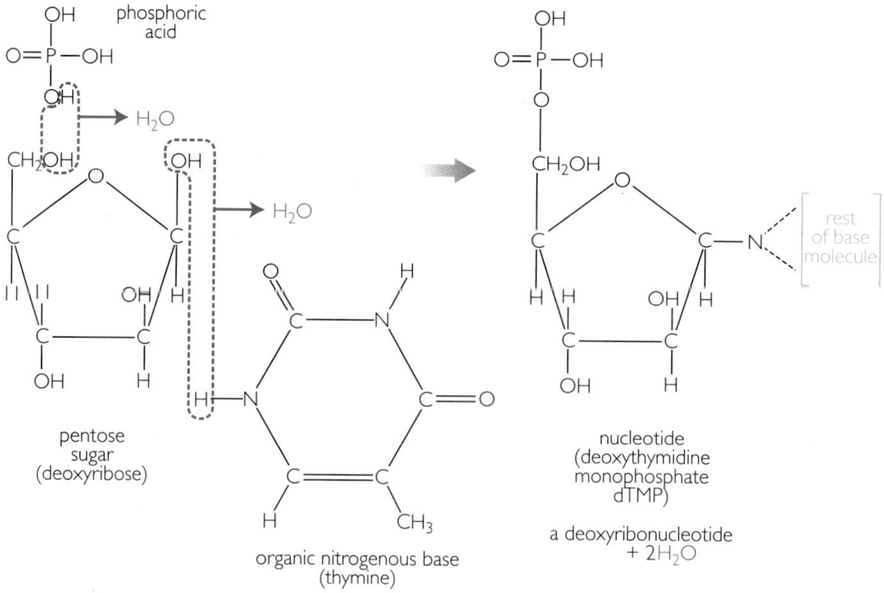

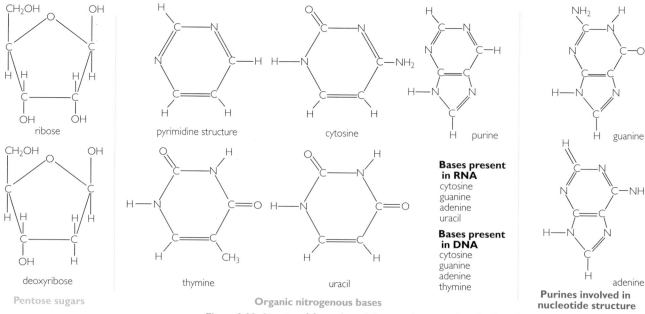

Figure 2.27 *Formation of a nucleotide by condensation of an organic nitrogenous base, a pentose sugar and a molecule of phosphoric acid*

ribose ($C_5H_{10}O_5$). Nucleotides containing ribose, referred to as ribonucleotides, are involved in the formation of ribonucleic acid (RNA) and those containing deoxyribose are deoxyribonucleotides, found in deoxyribonucleic acid (DNA). The organic bases present in nucleotides are either **pyrimidines**, which have a single-ring structure, or **purines** with a double ring structure. **Cytosine**, **thymine** and **uracil** are pyrimidines and the purines are **adenine** and **guanine**. These bases form links with the carbon–1 of the pentose. Adenine, cytosine and guanine are present in both types of nucleotides. In addition, uracil may be present in ribonucleotides and thymine in deoxyribonucleotides (Figure 2.28).

Bases present in RNA
cytosine
guanine
adenine
uracil

Bases present in DNA
cytosine
guanine
adenine
thymine

Pentose sugars

Organic nitrogenous bases

Purines involved in nucleotide structure

Figure 2.28 *Structural formulae of the constituent molecules found in RNA (ribonucleic acid) and DNA (deoxyribonucleic acid): the pentose sugars and the purine and pyrimidine bases*

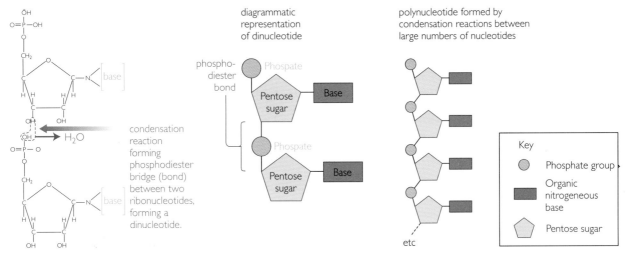

Figure 2.29 *Formation of a polynucleotide by repeated condensation of nucleotides*

Apart from their involvement in the formation of the nucleic acids, nucleotides and related compounds have important roles in cells. Adenosine triphosphate (ATP), a ribonucleotide with three phosphate groups attached to the pentose, acts as an energy storage molecule. When the phosphate group at the end is removed by hydrolysis, energy is released, which can be used for metabolic reactions in cells. Molecules of ATP can be built up, using energy from respiration, by the addition of a phosphate group to adenosine diphosphate (ADP). Other derivatives of nucleotides, such as nicotinamide adenine dinucleotide (NAD), nicotinamide adenine dinucleotide phosphate (NADP) and coenzyme A, are involved in metabolic reactions discussed later.

A dinucleotide is formed when a condensation reaction occurs between the phosphate group of one nucleotide and the pentose of another. More nucleotides can be added, building up a long polynucleotide chain. Phosphodiester bonds link the nucleotides together (Figure 2.29). Such bonds are covalent and contribute to the stability of the polynucleotide.

The structure of DNA

DNA is a polymer of deoxyribonucleotides. The nucleotides join when covalent, phosphodiester bonds are formed between the carbon–3 of the pentose of one and the phosphate group of the next, giving rise to a sugar-phosphate backbone with the bases projecting outwards. DNA is double stranded, so two polynucleotide chains are involved. Each chain has a 5′ end and a 3′ end. At the 5′ end, the carbon–5 of the pentose residue of the nucleotide is nearest the end, and at the 3′ end it is the carbon–3 of the pentose residue that is closest to the end. The two chains coil around each other forming a **double helix**, which is held together by hydrogen bonds between opposite bases, called base pairs. Pairing only occurs between a purine and a pyrimidine. In DNA, adenine can only pair with thymine and guanine with cytosine. So that the base pairing can occur, the chains are anti-parallel: one chain runs from 5′ to 3′ and the other from 3′ to 5′. It has been determined that the base pairs are 0.34 nm apart and that there are ten base pairs in one complete turn of the helix (Figure 2.30). Because of the rules of base pairing, the sequence of bases along one of the polynucleotide chains determines the sequence along the other.

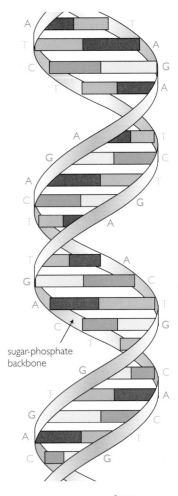

Figure 2.30 *Structure of DNA, illustrating the so-called 'double helix' of paired polynucleotide strands running in opposite directions (3′ → 5′ and 5′ → 3′)*

3 Enzymes

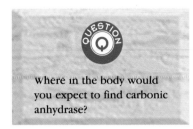

QUESTION

Where in the body would you expect to find carbonic anhydrase?

Enzymes as organic catalysts

Enzymes are substances that act as catalysts, in other words they increase the **rate** of chemical reactions. Consider the following general reaction between two substances, A and B, which react together to form a product, substance C:

$$A + B \rightarrow C$$

In biological systems, this reaction might occur very slowly, or not at all, in the absence of an enzyme. Enzymes will greatly increase the rate of formation of the product. Enzymes can increase the rate of reactions by a factor of at least a million. One of the fastest enzymes known is carbonic anhydrase, which catalyses the following reaction:

$$CO_2 + H_2O \rightleftharpoons H_2CO_3$$

Carbonic anhydrase reacts with 10^5 molecules of carbon dioxide per second.

Most enzymes are large protein molecules, with complex three-dimensional shapes, but recently it has become clear that substances other than proteins have catalytic properties. In 1983, Thomas Cech at University of Colorado discovered in *Tetrahymena* ciliate protozoan, a type of RNA with such properties. This catalytic RNA was termed **ribozyme**, and is involved in the removal of part of a large RNA molecule and the subsequent joining together of the remaining parts to form a functional RNA molecule. Similar activity has since been found in the cells of some bacteria and fungi.

Unlike chemical catalysts, such as manganese dioxide, enzymes are specific. This means that each enzyme will normally only catalyse one reaction. The substance with which the enzyme combines is known as the **substrate**, which combines with the enzyme at a particular place on the enzyme's surface called the **active site**. Enzyme molecules are usually very much larger than their substrates, and the active site is only a relatively small part of the enzyme, consisting of only 3 to 12 amino acid residues. The rest of the enzyme molecule is involved in maintaining the shape of the active site. The precise shape of the active site is important because it is complementary to the shape of the substrate molecule, which fits into the active site by what is often known as the 'lock-and-key mechanism'. However, it is now clear that the shape of the active site of some enzymes changes when the substrate molecule attaches to it. This process is referred to as **induced fit**. The substrate molecule joins with the active site of the enzyme to form an enzyme–substrate complex (Figure 3.1).

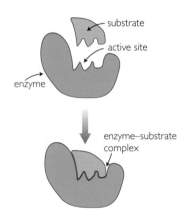

Figure 3.1 Lock-and-key model of enzyme action, in which a substrate molecule and an enzyme molecule interact at a specific active site on the enzyme, forming a temporary enzyme–substrate complex

Energy and chemical reactions

When chemical reactions occur, energy changes result from the changes in structure of the reactants, breaking and reforming chemical bonds. These energy changes are in the form of heat. Some reactions produce heat, others absorb heat. A reaction such as combustion, which produces heat, is known as **exothermic**, but if heat is taken in, it is called an **endothermic** reaction. Most reactions that occur spontaneously are exothermic. In living organisms, energy produced in a reaction can take various forms, such as heat, light or chemical energy. Heat and light will be dissipated, and therefore will not be available to the organism for other processes. Other forms of energy can be used by the organism to drive other processes. These forms of energy are known as 'free energy'. Change in free energy is given the symbol ΔG. A reaction will only occur spontaneously if ΔG is negative. In this case the reaction is termed **exergonic**. If ΔG is positive, an input of free energy will be needed to drive the reaction, which is said to be **endergonic**. In biological systems, endergonic reactions include the synthesis of macromolecules, such as proteins, and these reactions are linked to exergonic reactions, which provide the free energy required.

In living cells, most chemical reactions require an input of energy before the molecules will react together. This is referred to as the **activation energy**. Imagine a boulder near the top of a steep hill (Figure 3.2). Before the boulder can roll down the other side of the hill, you would have to push it to the top, in other words put some energy in, before it will roll down.

This can be likened to the progress of a chemical reaction, the boulder near the top represents the energy level of the reactants and the energy you have to put in to push the boulder to the very top represents the free energy of activation. Once the reactants reach this point, the reaction will proceed spontaneously, as the boulder rolls down and the products are formed.

Enzymes increase the rates of reactions by reducing the free energy of activation, so that the barrier to a reaction occurring is lower in the presence of an enzyme. The combination of enzyme and substrate creates a new energy profile, for the reaction, with a lower free energy of activation (Figure 3.3).

Once the products have been formed, they leave the active site of the enzyme, which is left free to combine with a new substrate molecule. Enzymes, like chemical catalysts, are not used up in the reaction they catalyse so they can be used over and over again many times. The overall reaction between an enzyme and its substrate can be represented by the following equation:

ENZYME + SUBSTRATE → ENZYME–SUBSTRATE complex → ENZYME + PRODUCTS

Factors affecting enzyme activity

Enzymes, being proteins, are sensitive to changes in their environment. Changes in temperature and pH can cause changes in the shape of the enzyme molecule and will therefore affect its activity. Changes in the concentration of both the enzyme and its substrate will also affect the rate of an enzyme-catalysed reaction.

Temperature

Temperature has a complex effect on enzyme activity (see Practical: The effect of temperature on the activity of trypsin). On one hand, a rise in temperature

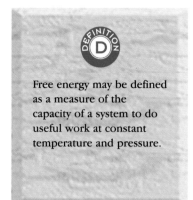

Free energy may be defined as a measure of the capacity of a system to do useful work at constant temperature and pressure.

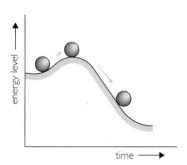

Figure 3.2 Graph to illustrate the boulder analogy of a reaction, in which activation energy needs to be added to a system to initiate the reaction

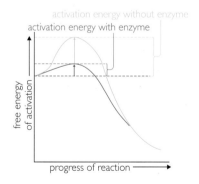

Figure 3.3 Graph to illustrate how addition of an enzyme lowers the amount of activation energy needed to initiate the reaction

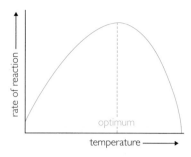

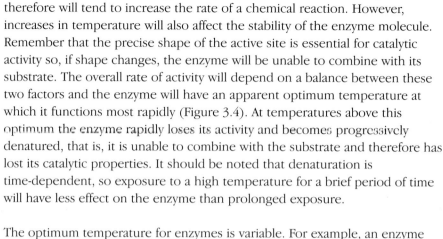

will increase the kinetic energy of enzyme and substrate molecules, and therefore will tend to increase the rate of a chemical reaction. However, increases in temperature will also affect the stability of the enzyme molecule. Remember that the precise shape of the active site is essential for catalytic activity so, if shape changes, the enzyme will be unable to combine with its substrate. The overall rate of activity will depend on a balance between these two factors and the enzyme will have an apparent optimum temperature at which it functions most rapidly (Figure 3.4). At temperatures above this optimum the enzyme rapidly loses its activity and becomes progressively denatured, that is, it is unable to combine with the substrate and therefore has lost its catalytic properties. It should be noted that denaturation is time-dependent, so exposure to a high temperature for a brief period of time will have less effect on the enzyme than prolonged exposure.

Figure 3.4 Graph to illustrate the effect of temperature on enzyme activity, showing that enzymes have an optimum temperature at which reaction rate is at its maximum

The optimum temperature for enzymes is variable. For example, an enzyme known as Taq polymerase, a DNA polymerase extracted from *Thermus aquaticus* (a bacterium that lives in hot springs), is stable up to 95 °C. Many enzymes, however, function most efficiently at about 40 °C.

pH

Most enzymes have a characteristic pH at which they function most efficiently (see Practical: The effect of pH on the activity of catalase). This is known as the optimum pH. Changes in pH affect the ionisation of side groups in the enzyme's amino acid residues. This in turn affects the overall shape of the enzyme molecule and affects the efficiency of formation of enzyme–substrate complexes. At extremes of pH the enzyme molecule may become denatured. As with optimum temperatures, enzymes have varying optimum pH values. Although many enzymes have optima at pH values of around 7 (neutral), there are some that function best at extreme values. As an example, pepsins, which are protein-digesting enzymes found in the stomach, have unusually low pH optima, in the range 1.5 to 3.5. At the other extreme, arginase, an enzyme involved in the synthesis of urea in the liver, has an optimum pH of 10. The optimum pH for an enzyme is not necessarily the same as the pH of its normal surroundings. This is one way in which the intracellular environment can control enzyme activity. A typical graph of rate of reaction plotted against pH, produced experimentally by determining the activity of an enzyme at a range of specific pH values, shows a bell-shaped curve. You will notice that, unlike the curve for enzyme activity plotted against temperature, this is a symmetrical shape (Figure 3.5).

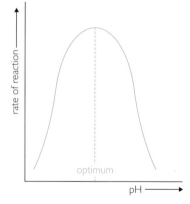

Figure 3.5 Graph to illustrate the effect of pH on enzyme activity, showing that enzymes have an optimum pH at which reaction rate is at its maximum

Concentration

Both enzyme and substrate concentration affect the rate of reaction (see *Practical: The effect of enzyme concentration of the activity of amylase*, page 46). Clearly, as the concentration of enzyme increases, the number of active sites also increase. Provided that there is an excess of substrate molecules, the rate of reaction increases in proportion to the concentration of enzyme. A graph of rate of reaction plotted against enzyme concentration is a straight line (Figure 3.6).

Consider what will happen if the substrate concentration increases, but the concentration of enzyme molecules remains the same. Since the rate of reaction depends on the rate of formation of enzyme–substrate complexes, the rate of reaction will increase as the substrate concentration increases, but only until all enzyme molecules are being used. After this point, no matter how much more substrate is added, the enzymes are working as fast as they can, so the rate reaches a maximum velocity and remains constant. This rate is referred to as V_{max}. Figure 3.7 shows the effect of substrate concentration on the rate of reaction.

Inhibitors

Inhibitors are substances that reduce the activity of enzymes. They act by interfering with the activity of the active site, either directly or indirectly. There are several different types of inhibitors, which can be either reversible (if they bind reversibly with the enzyme) or irreversible (if they bind permanently to the enzyme).

Some reversible inhibitors bind to the active site of the enzyme. These are known as competitive inhibitors because they will compete for the active site with the normal substrate. Many competitive inhibitors have a similar shape to the substrate and will bind to the active site, preventing the substrate from binding to the same active site. The presence of the inhibitor will therefore reduce the rate of reaction, but competitive inhibitors can be displaced from the active site by the substrate if the substrate is in high concentration, restoring catalytic activity. An example of a competitive inhibitor is malonate, which competes for the active site on the enzyme succinate dehydrogenase. This enzyme removes two hydrogen atoms from succinate, forming fumarate, but is unable to do so from malonate.

Irreversible inhibitors attach tightly to the enzyme molecule so that it loses its catalytic properties. Irreversible inhibitors include ions of heavy metals, such as mercury and certain nerve gases. Di-isopropylphosphofluoridate (DIPF) is one such compound, which reacts with the active site of acetylcholinesterase, completely inactivating this enzyme.

Enzymes and metabolic pathways

The sum total of all the reactions occurring in cells is referred to as metabolism. Metabolism consists of hundreds of linked chemical reactions, making up particular metabolic pathways, such as the breakdown of glucose to produce carbon dioxide and water. These reactions usually occur in a series of small steps, rather than just one reaction. A metabolic pathway can be illustrated by the following simple diagram, where each letter represents one substance.

$$A + B \rightarrow C \rightarrow D + E$$

Each single reaction in this series will be catalysed by a specific enzyme, so we could add these to the pathway:

$$\begin{array}{ccc} & \text{enzyme X} & \text{enzyme Y} \\ A + B & \rightarrow \quad C & \rightarrow \quad D + E \end{array}$$

If A and B represent the reactants, and D and E the final products, then

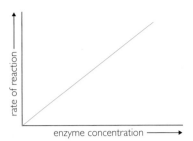

Figure 3.6 Graph to illustrate the effect of enzyme concentration on the rate of a reaction, showing that addition of enzyme increases reaction rate linearly

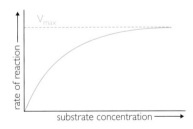

Figure 3.7 Graph to illustrate the effect of substrate concentration on the rate of a reaction, showing that addition of substrate increases reaction rate until the enzyme is saturated, at which point the maximum rate of the reaction (V_{max}) is reached

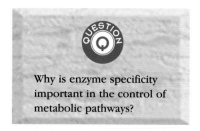

Why is enzyme specificity important in the control of metabolic pathways?

substance C is referred to as an intermediate, which is converted by enzyme Y to the final products. To illustrate a metabolic pathway, here is the first part of the process known as glycolysis. Glycolysis is a series of reactions involving the breakdown of glucose, via a series of intermediates, to form a substance called pyruvate. (Glycolysis is described in more detail in Chapter 4).

$$\text{Glucose + ATP} \xrightarrow{\text{hexokinase}} \text{Glucose 6-phosphate + ADP + H}^+$$

$$\downarrow \text{ phosphoglucose isomerase}$$

$$\text{Fructose 6-phosphate}$$

Notice that each of these two reactions is catalysed by a specific enzyme; in one it is hexokinase and in the other it is phosphoglucose isomerase.

Classification of enzymes

There are very many different enzymes (over 2000 have been named and studied in detail), and they are grouped according to the type of reaction they catalyse. There are six major groups, as shown in Table 3.1.

Table 3.1 *Enzyme classification according to reaction type*

Group	Type of reaction catalysed	Example of enzyme
oxidoreductases	removal or addition of hydrogen atoms (oxidation or reduction)	succinate dehydrogenase
transferases	transfer of a group from one compound to another	aminotransferase
hydrolases	hydrolysis	sucrase
lyases	elimination of a group to form a double bond	citrate lyase
isomerases	intramolecular rearrangements	phosphoglucose isomerase
ligases	formation of a bond, coupled with ATP hydrolysis	glycogen synthetase

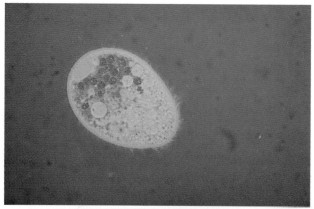

Figure 3.8 The ciliate protozoan Tetrahymena

The effect of temperature on the activity of trypsin

Introduction

Casein is a protein found in milk. When a suspension of casein is hydrolysed, the suspension starts cloudy but becomes clearer as the products dissolve. This hydrolysis is catalysed by proteolytic enzymes such as trypsin. The aim of this experiment is to investigate the effect of temperature on the activity of trypsin, using a suspension of casein as the substrate. Changes in the clarity of the casein suspension will be easier to see if the tubes are checked periodically by holding them against a piece of black card.

Materials

- Casein suspension, 4 per cent
- Trypsin solution, 0.5 per cent
- Distilled water
- Test tubes and rack
- Graduated pipettes or syringes
- Glass beakers or water baths
- Thermometer
- Black card
- Stopwatch

Method

1 Set up a water bath at 30 °C.
2 Pipette 5 cm^3 of casein suspension into one test tube and 5 cm^3 of trypsin solution into another tube.
3 Stand both tubes in the water bath and leave them for several minutes to reach the temperature of the water bath.
4 Meanwhile, set up a control tube containing 5 cm^3 of casein suspension plus 5 cm^3 of distilled water. Stand this tube in the water bath.
5 Mix the enzyme and substrate together and replace the tube in the water bath. Start a stopwatch immediately.
6 Observe the contents of the tube carefully, checking against a piece of black card, and record the time taken for the suspension to become clear.
7 Repeat this procedure at a range of temperatures, for example between 25 °C and 65 °C. Use the same volumes of casein suspension and enzyme solution each time.

Results and discussion

1 Explain the function of the control tube.
2 Describe the relationship between temperature and the time taken for the casein suspension to clear.
3 Find the relative rate of reaction by working out the reciprocal of the time taken for the suspension to clear at each temperature.
4 Plot a graph of the rate of reaction against temperature.
5 Explain your results as fully as you can.
6 What are the sources of error in this experiment? How could it be improved?

ENZYMES

The effect of pH on the activity of catalase

Introduction

Catalase, an enzyme found in many different tissues, catalyses the breakdown of hydrogen peroxide into water and oxygen:

$$2H_2O_2 \rightarrow 2H_2O + O_2$$

Hydrogen peroxide is a toxic substance that can be formed during aerobic respiration and catalase removes this product. The activity of catalase can be measured by finding the rate of oxygen release from hydrogen peroxide.

Minced potato provides a suitable source of catalase and the pH is varied in this experiment using citric acid-sodium phosphate buffer solutions at pH values of 4.4, 5.2, 6.5 and 7.5.

Materials

IRRITANT
citric
acid

- Citric acid–sodium phosphate buffer solutions. These are made up as follows. Solution A is 21 g citric acid·H_2O dm^{-3}. Solution B is 28.4 g anhydrous disodium hydrogen phosphate (Na_2HPO_4) dm^{-3}. Buffer solutions of each pH are prepared by mixing solutions A and B in the volumes shown in Table 3.2.

Table 3.2 *Composition of citric acid–sodium phosphate buffer solutions at various pHs*

pH	Solution A / cm^3	Solution B/cm^3
4.4	27.9	22.1
5.2	23.2	26.8
6.5	14.5	35.5
7.5	3.9	46.1

CORROSIVE

OXIDISING
hydrogen
peroxide

- Hydrogen peroxide solution, 10 volume
- Minced potato
- 5 cm^3 or 10 cm^3 plastic syringe with the end cut off, to measure minced potato
- Graduated pipette or syringe to measure buffer solutions
- Stopwatch

Method

1 Set up the apparatus as shown in Figure 3.10.

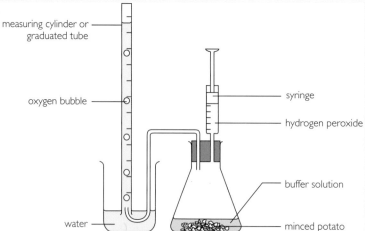

measuring cylinder or graduated tube

oxygen bubble

water

syringe

hydrogen peroxide

buffer solution

minced potato

Figure 3.10 Apparatus for the collection of oxygen produced by the decomposition of hydrogen peroxide, catalysed by the enzyme catalase

2 Place 3 cm^3 of minced potato in the conical flask and add 10 cm^3 of buffer solution. Swirl gently to mix.

3 Replace the bung in the flask ensuring an airtight seal. Fill the graduated tube with water and invert carefully into the beaker of water. Do not place over the end of the delivery tube.

4 Measure 5 cm^3 of hydrogen peroxide into the syringe and connect to the flask. Inject the hydrogen peroxide. This will displace air which must not enter the graduated tube.

5 Immediately position the graduated tube over the end of the delivery tube and measure the volume of oxygen collected every 30 seconds for 5 minutes.

6 Repeat the experiment using a different buffer solution and fresh potato.

Results and discussion

1 Tabulate your results and plot a graph to show the volumes of oxygen evolved against time for each buffer solution.

2 At which pH value was catalase
   (a) most active?
   (b) least active?

3 Which factors were kept constant in this experiment?

4 What were the possible sources of error and how could they be minimised?

5 Explain why changes in pH affect enzyme activity.

Further work

1 This apparatus could be used to investigate other factors affecting catalase activity, such as enzyme or substrate concentration. Enzyme concentration can be varied by using different volumes of potato, for example, 1, 2 and 4 cm^3 of minced potato could be used at pH 6.3, and with a constant concentration and volume of hydrogen peroxide.

2 The substrate concentration can be varied by using 2.5, 5, 10 and 20 volume strengths of hydrogen peroxide. Each time, 5.0 cm^3 of hydrogen peroxide should be used, at pH 6.3 and with a constant 3.0 cm^3 of minced potato.

ENZYMES

The effect of enzyme concentration on the activity of amylase

Introduction

Amylase is an enzyme that is present in both saliva and pancreatic juice. Its function is to catalyse the hydrolysis of amylose and amylopectin to a mixture of products, including maltose and dextrin. Maltose consists of two α-glucose residues joined by a 1,4 linkage; dextrin is made up of several α-glucose units joined by both 1,4 and 1,6 linkages.

This experiment is to investigate the effect of amylase concentration on its activity. The relative activity of amylase is found by noting the time taken for the starch substrate to be broken down, that is, when it no longer gives a blue-black colour when tested with iodine solution. This time is referred to as the achromatic point.

Materials

CARE!

- Amylase solution, 0.1 per cent. This must be made up freshly.
- Starch solution, 1.0 per cent. A mixture of equal volumes of the amylase and starch solutions incubated at 35 °C should give a negative result when tested for starch after two to three minutes. If necessary, the concentration of starch should be increased or decreased.
- Distilled water
- Iodine in potassium iodide solution
- White tile and glass rod
- Graduated pipettes or syringes
- Pasteur pipettes
- Test tubes and rack
- Glass beaker or water bath
- Thermometer
- Stopwatch

Method

1 Prepare four different concentrations of the enzyme solution: undiluted, diluted to a half, diluted to a quarter, and diluted to one tenth of the original concentrations. The volumes of enzyme solution and distilled water to use are shown in Table 3.3.

Table 3.3 *Composition of amylase solutions made from a 0.1 per cent stock solution*

Volume of amylase solution/cm^3	Volume of distilled water/cm^3	Final amylase concentration
5.0	5.0	0.5
2.5	7.5	0.25
1.0	9.0	0.1

2 Set up a water bath at 35 °C.
3 Pipette 5 cm^3 of the undiluted enzyme solution into one test tube and 5 cm^3 of starch solution into another test tube. Stand both tubes in the water bath and leave for several minutes to reach the temperature of the water bath.
4 Mix the enzyme and starch solutions together, replace the mixture in the water bath and immediately start a stop watch.
5 At intervals of one minute, remove a drop of the mixture and test it with iodine solution on a white tile.
6 Continue the experiment until the mixture fails to give a blue-black colour with iodine solution. Record this as the achromatic point.

7 Repeat this procedure with the other concentrations of amylase. Use exactly 5 cm³ of enzyme solution and 5 cm³ of starch solution each time.

Results and discussion

1 Tabulate your results carefully. The relative rate of reaction can be calculated by finding the reciprocal of the time taken to reach the achromatic point at each concentration of amylase.

2 Plot a graph to show the relative rate of reaction against enzyme concentration.

3 Explain your results as fully as you can.

4 What are the sources of error in this experiment? How could it be improved?

4 Metabolic pathways

The role of enzymes in metabolic pathways is outlined in Chapter 3. Here we look at cellular respiration as an example of a metabolic pathway.

Cellular respiration and ATP

All living organisms require an input of free energy for three major purposes: to be able to perform mechanical work, such as muscle contraction and cell movement, the active transport of ions and other substances across cell surface membranes, and for the synthesis of macromolecules. This free energy is obtained from the environment. Chemotrophic organisms obtain this energy by oxidising organic foodstuffs, such as glucose, whereas phototrophic organisms obtain it by trapping light energy (Figure 4.1).

The oxidation of foodstuffs to obtain free energy is known as cellular respiration. Cellular respiration occurs as a series of linked, enzyme-catalysed reactions. These reactions can be grouped into three main stages: **glycolysis**, the **Krebs cycle**, and **oxidative phosphorylation**.

The most important product of cellular respiration is **adenosine triphosphate** (ATP). A molecule of ATP consists of adenine (a nucleotide base) linked to ribose (a five-carbon sugar). The sugar is, in turn, linked to three inorganic phosphate groups. The structure of ATP is shown in Figure 4.2.

ATP is often described as the universal currency of free energy in cells. It is important because the phosphoanhydride bonds, when hydrolysed, yield a relatively large amount of free energy. ATP can be hydrolysed to adenosine diphosphate (ADP) and inorganic phosphate (P_i), as shown below:

$$ATP + H_2O \rightarrow ADP + P_i + H^+ \qquad \Delta G = -30 \text{ kJ mol}^{-1}$$

Notice that because G is negative, this reaction is exergonic, in other words, it yields free energy. This free energy can be used to drive reactions that require an input of free energy, such as active transport. ATP is rapidly re-synthesised from ADP and P_i when foodstuffs are oxidised in chemotrophic organisms or when light energy is trapped by autotrophic organisms.

ATP functions as an immediate source of free energy in living cells, rather than as a long-term energy store. The rate of production and use of ATP is very high. In a typical cell, one ATP molecule is used within one minute of its formation.

Figure 4.1 Green plants are phototrophic organisms: they obtain free energy by trapping light energy

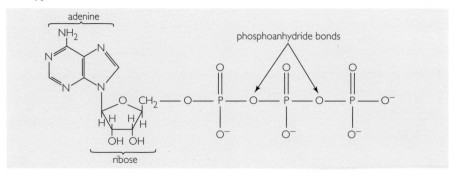

Figure 4.2 Structure of ATP (adenosine triphosphate), showing phosphoanhydride bonds

Electron carriers

Many reactions in metabolic pathways involve the oxidation of a substrate by the removal of electrons (e^-) or hydrogen atoms (H). Electrons are transferred to a group of special substances known as electron carriers (or hydrogen carriers). The reduced forms of these carriers eventually transfer their electrons to oxygen by means of a chain of electron carriers situated in the inner mitochondrial membrane. ATP is formed from ADP and P_i as a result of this flow of electrons.

One of the most important electron carriers is nicotinamide adenine dinucleotide (NAD^+). When a substrate is oxidised, NAD^+ accepts a hydrogen ion (H^+) and two electrons. The reduced form of this carrier is called NADH. This reaction is shown below.

$$NAD^+ + 2H^+ + 2e^- \rightarrow NADH + H^+$$

One hydrogen atom from the substrate is transferred to NAD^+, the other appears in solution. Both electrons are transferred to part of the NAD^+ molecule.

Other electron carriers include flavin adenine dinucleotide (FAD) and nicotinamide adenine dinucleotide phosphate ($NADP^+$). The importance of reduced electron carriers is that the change from the reduced form back to the oxidised form of the carrier is linked to the synthesis of ATP.

Glycolysis

Glycolysis occurs in the cytoplasm of cells and consists of a series of enzyme-catalysed reactions in which each molecule of glucose is converted step-by-step into two molecules of pyruvate. Pyruvate is a compound that contains three carbon atoms and links glycolysis with the reactions that follow.

Initially, glucose is phosphorylated by ATP to form glucose 6-phosphate:

$$\text{glucose + ATP} \xrightarrow{\text{hexokinase}} \text{glucose 6-phosphate + ADP + } H^+$$

Each of the six carbon atoms in the glucose molecule is numbered according to a conventional system. The number 6 in the equation above refers to a particular carbon atom in the glucose molecule. The structure of glucose 6-phosphate is shown in Figure 4.3.

Similarly, in the other compounds that follow, the numbers refer to particular carbon atoms in the compounds.

Phosphorylation of glucose serves two purposes. Firstly, it prevents glucose from leaving the cell, because the membrane is impermeable to sugar phosphates, and secondly, phosphorylation makes glucose more reactive, so that it can be readily converted into phosphorylated three-carbon compounds.

The individual reactions of glycolysis are shown in Figure 4.4. The number of carbon atoms is each compound is shown in square brackets.

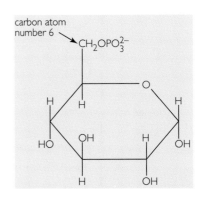

Figure 4.3 Structure of glucose 6-phosphate, produced in the reaction catalysed by hexokinase

Figure 4.4 shows all the individual steps of glycolysis, but we can simplify it to show just a few important stages (Figure 4.5). The numbers in square brackets indicate the number of carbon atoms in each compound.

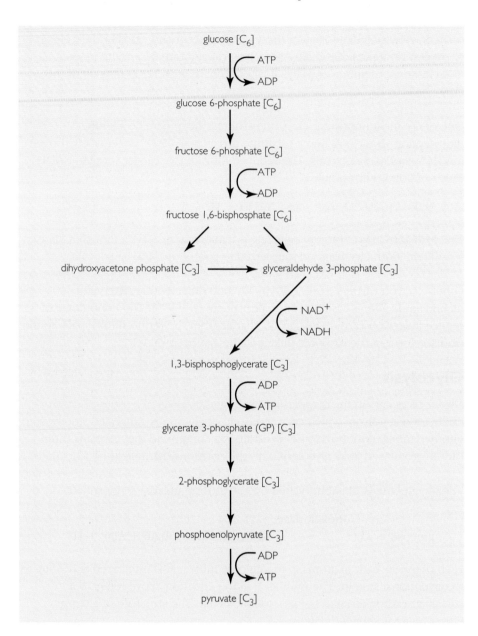

Figure 4.4 *Stages in glycolysis, in which one molecule of glucose is broken down into two molecules of pyruvate, with the net generation of two molecules of ATP*

Remember that two three-carbon compounds are produced from each molecule of glucose, so although two molecules of ATP are used in glycolysis, four molecules are produced, giving a net production of two molecules of ATP per molecule of glucose. This is summarised in Table 4.1.

The products of glycolysis are, therefore, pyruvate, ATP and NADH. If oxygen is present, pyruvate passes into a mitochondrion and the sequence of reactions known as the Krebs cycle occurs.

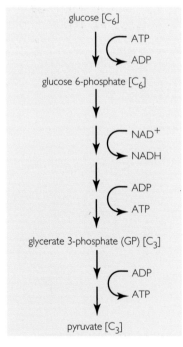

Figure 4.5 Summary of the essential stages in glycolysis

Table 4.1 *Consumption and generation of ATP in glycolysis*

Reaction	ATP change per molecule of glucose
glucose $\rightarrow$ glucose 6-phosphate	−1
fructose 6-phosphate $\rightarrow$ fructose 1,6-bisphosphate	−1
2 × 1,3-bisphosphoglycerate $\rightarrow$ 2 × 3-phosphoglycerate	+2
2 × phosphoenolpyruvate $\rightarrow$ 2 × pyruvate	+2
	net +2

The Krebs cycle

In aerobic respiration only, the pyruvate, which was produced by glycolysis, passes into the matrix of a mitochondrion. Here, the link reaction occurs, in which pyruvate is converted into acetate and combined with a compound called coenzyme A, to form acetyl coenzyme A. This is often abbreviated to acetyl CoA. During this reaction, NADH and carbon dioxide are also formed:

$$\text{pyruvate} + \text{NAD}^+ + \text{CoA} \rightarrow \text{acetyl CoA} + \text{NADH} + \text{CO}_2$$

The Krebs cycle (also known as the tricarboxylic acid cycle, or TCA cycle) is named after Sir Hans Krebs (Figure 4.6) who, in 1937, pieced together this series of reactions. In the Krebs cycle, a four-carbon compound, oxaloacetate, combines with the two-carbon acetyl unit from acetyl CoA, to form a six-carbon compound, citrate. A sequence of reactions occurs, all of which are catalysed by enzymes present in the mitochondrial matrix, in which citrate is converted back

Figure 4.6 Sir Hans Krebs, who discovered the reactions that make up the cycle that bears his name, for which he was awarded the Nobel Prize for medicine in 1953

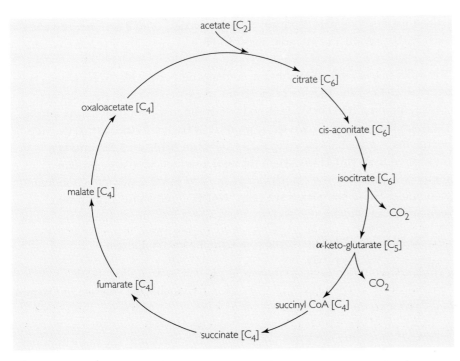

Figure 4.7 Stages in the Krebs cycle, in which pyruvate is progressively oxidised and decarboxylated, releasing carbon dioxide and hydrogen atoms which are taken up by hydrogen carriers

to oxaloacetate. The complete Krebs cycle is shown in Figure 4.7. The numbers in square brackets indicate the number of carbon atoms in each compound.

Since citrate has six carbon atoms and oxaloacetate has four, two carbon atoms must be lost during one turn of the cycle. These exit the cycle in the form of carbon dioxide. Also, several reactions result in the removal of hydrogen from intermediates and both NAD and FAD are reduced (see Practical: Use of a redox indicator to show dehydrogenase activity). One molecule of ATP is also synthesised.

We can summarise the overall reaction of the Krebs cycle as follows:
- Two carbon atoms enter the cycle and two carbon atoms are lost as carbon dioxide.
- One molecule of ATP is synthesised.
- Four pairs of hydrogen atoms are removed, two NAD^+ molecules are reduced to NADH and one FAD molecule is reduced to $FADH_2$.

All the molecules of reduced electron carriers produced by both glycolysis and the Krebs cycle are re-oxidised in the electron transport chain (ETC). During this process, a large amount of free energy is liberated, which can be used to generate ATP. The enzymes for this process are fixed in the folded inner membrane of the mitochondrion. We will now have a look at this process in some detail.

Oxidative phosphorylation

Oxidative phosphorylation is the process by which ATP is formed when electrons are transferred from NADH or $FADH_2$ to oxygen, by a series of electron carriers. This is the major source of ATP in aerobic organisms. The oxidation of each NADH produces three molecules of ATP and the oxidation of each $FADH_2$ produces two molecules of ATP.

The inner mitochondrial membrane contains numerous electron carriers, such as cytochromes. The transfer of electrons to oxygen through these carriers leads to protons (H^+) being pumped out of the mitochondrial matrix into the intermembrane space. When the protons flow back into the matrix, the free energy made available is used to make ATP from ADP and P_i. Electrons are transferred from NADH to oxygen through a sequence of large protein complexes, including the cytochromes, situated in the inner mitochondrial membrane. These complexes are called NADH-Q reductase, cytochrome reductase, and cytochrome oxidase. These are shown diagrammatically below.

NADH → NADH-Q reductase → Cytochrome reductase →
(I)   (II)

Cytochrome oxidase → Oxygen
(III)

Figure 4.8 shows the movement of protons (H^+) back into the mitochondrial matrix and ATP synthesis. The three groups of electron carriers are labelled I, II, and III, as in the reaction shown above.

QUESTION

How many molecules of ATP, NADH and $FADH_2$ will be produced from one molecule of glucose? Hint: remember that each glucose molecule produces two molecules of pyruvate.

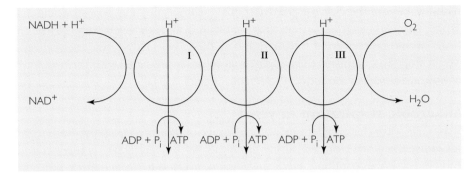

Figure 4.8 Simplified scheme for oxidative phosphorylation, in which hydrogen ions (protons) are transported by a series of carrier molecules – the electron transport chain – across the inner mitochondrial membrane, accompanied by generation of ATP and water

Oxygen acts as the final electron acceptor and is reduced to form water as shown in the equation below:

$$O_2 + 4H^+ + 4e^- \rightarrow 2H_2O$$

Water is therefore the final product of oxidative phosphorylation.

Yield of ATP from complete oxidation of glucose

We can now work out the total yield of ATP from the complete oxidation of glucose. This is shown in Table 4.2.

Table 4.2 *The total yield of ATP from the complete oxidation of glucose*

Source of ATP	ATP yield per glucose molecule
Glycolysis	+2
Krebs cycle	+2
2 × NADH formed in glycolysis	+4
2 × NADH formed in link reaction	+6
2 × FADH$_2$ formed in Krebs cycle	+4
6 × NADH formed in Krebs cycle	+18
	Total +36

The complete oxidation of glucose, under standard laboratory conditions, yields 2870 kJ mol^{-1}. The total free energy stored in 36 ATP is 1100 kJ, so the overall efficiency of ATP formation from glucose is

$$(1100 \div 2870) \times 100 = 38\%$$

The total yield of ATP from the complete oxidation of glucose is 36 molecules per molecule of glucose in enkaryotic cells. In prokaryotic cells, the yield is 38 per molecule of glucose.

Anaerobic respiration

So far, we have followed the fate of a glucose molecule when it is completely oxidised, to form carbon dioxide, water and ATP. Many bacteria can only live without oxygen and some organisms, such as yeast, can live with or without oxygen. If oxygen is present, yeast respires aerobically, but in the absence of oxygen, yeast respires **anaerobically**.

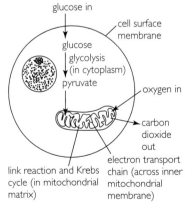

Figure 4.9 Summary diagram to show the sites of glycolysis, the link reaction, Krebs cycle and the electron transport chain in a eukaryotic cell

Figure 4.10 In the hard-working muscles of this athlete, pyruvate is reduced to lactate in the absence of oxygen, and can build up in the muscles, causing cramp

Compare the yields of ATP from one molecule of glucose under aerobic and anaerobic conditions. What percentage of the total ATP available can be obtained via anaerobic respiration?

Without oxygen, the electron transport chain cannot function, so you would expect reduced electron carriers to accumulate in the cell. Eventually, all the NAD^+ would be converted to NADH and all the FAD to $FADH_2$ and metabolism would stop. So organisms that respire anaerobically are faced with the problem of how to re-oxidise the reduced electron carriers.

Anaerobic respiration in yeast

Yeast cells solve this problem by using a compound formed from pyruvate to re-oxidise the NADH formed during glycolysis. In this way, NAD^+ is regenerated and glycolysis can continue. Pyruvate is first converted to acetaldehyde by a decarboxylase enzyme, which removes carbon dioxide from pyruvate. Acetaldehyde is then reduced by NADH to give ethanol and NAD^+. The anaerobic breakdown of glucose by yeast is also known as **fermentation** and is the process responsible for producing beer and wine. Anaerobic respiration in yeast is summarised in Figure 4.11.

Anaerobic respiration in muscle

Anaerobic respiration can also occur in our muscles. This provides additional ATP, which enables muscles to contract even when they have used all their supplies of oxygen, such as during a brief period of vigorous physical exertion. In muscle tissue, pyruvate is reduced directly to lactate and NAD^+ is regenerated, so glycolysis can continue. The reduction of pyruvate to lactate is shown below:

$$\text{pyruvate} + \text{NADH} + H^+ \rightarrow \text{lactate} + NAD^+$$

The lactate accumulates in the muscle and, when the exercise is over, lactate is oxidised back to pyruvate. This requires additional oxygen, referred to as the oxygen debt. This additional oxygen is provided by deep and rapid breathing, which continues after the exercise.

Summary

Anaerobic respiration in yeast results in the formation of ethanol and carbon dioxide, whereas in muscle tissue, lactate is the final product. In both cases, the yield of ATP is the same as in glycolysis, that is, 2 molecules of ATP per molecule of glucose.

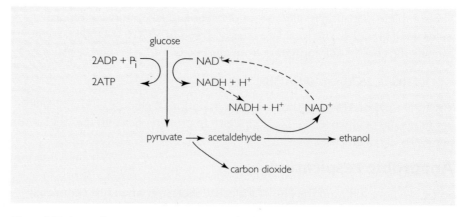

Figure 4.11 Anaerobic respiration in yeast, in which pyruvate is reduced to ethanol instead of entering the Krebs cycle

Use of a redox indicator to show dehydrogenase activity

Introduction

Triphenyl tetrazolium chloride (TTC) is an example of an artificial hydrogen acceptor, or redox indicator. TTC is colourless when oxidised, but forms red, insoluble compounds called formazans when reduced. TTC can therefore be used to show the presence of active dehydrogenase enzymes by a colour change. This experiment investigates the effect of temperature on the activity of dehydrogenases in yeast cells.

Materials

HARMFUL
triphenyl
tetrazolium
chloride

- Actively respiring yeast suspension. This should be prepared by adding 100 g of dried yeast to 1 dm^3 of water and mixing in 50 g glucose. This mixture should be allowed to stand in a large beaker for about two hours before the experiment
- Triphenyl tetrazolium chloride solution, 0.5 per cent
- Distilled water
- Test tubes and rack
- Graduated pipettes, or syringes
- Glass rods
- Crushed ice
- Beakers or water baths
- Thermometer
- Stopwatch

Method

1 Set up a water bath at 30 °C.
2 Pipette 10 cm^3 of yeast suspension into one test tube and 1 cm^3 of TTC solution into another test tube and stand them both in the water bath. Leave for several minutes to reach the temperature of the water bath.
3 Mix the yeast suspension and TTC solution together and return the test tube to the water bath. Start the stopwatch immediately.
4 Observe carefully and note the time taken for any colour changes to develop.
5 Repeat this procedure at a range of suitable temperatures, for example 20 °C, 40 °C and 50 °C.

Results and discussion

1 Explain why the yeast suspension and TTC solution were placed in the water bath before mixing together.
2 Plot a graph to show the relationship between temperature and the rate of activity of dehydrogenases.
3 If possible, try to find the optimum temperature for yeast dehydrogenases.
4 The effect of a 10 °C rise in temperature on the rate of a reaction can be expressed as the Q_{10} value. This is a ratio of the rate of a reaction at, for example, 30 °C to the rate of reaction at 20 °C. The Q_{10} value can be expressed as

$$Q_{10} = \frac{\text{rate at t + 10 °C}}{\text{rate at t °C}}$$

Determine the Q_{10} value for yeast respiration between the range of, for example, 30 °C and 40 °C.
5 What are the sources of error in this experiment? How could it be improved?
6 Outline the roles of dehydrogenases in cell respiration.

5 Chromosomes and the genetic code

Chromosome structure

Chromosomes in eukaryotic cells are made up of:
- DNA (deoxyribonucleic acid)
- proteins
- small amounts of RNA (ribonucleic acid).

Each human chromosome contains one very large molecule of DNA, which, if untangled from its protein, would measure 5 cm in length (Figure 5.1). The total length of DNA in the nucleus of a human cell has been estimated to be about 2.2 m. In order for this enormous length of DNA to fit into the nucleus, a great deal of folding and coiling is involved, especially when cells are undergoing nuclear division. Normally, when we use a microscope to look at the nuclei of cells, we cannot distinguish the chromosomes, but just before nuclear division takes place even more condensation occurs. This results in compact structures that can separate and move during cell division. The structure of nucleic acids is described in Chapter 2 and we now need to discuss how the protein and DNA are arranged in chromosomes.

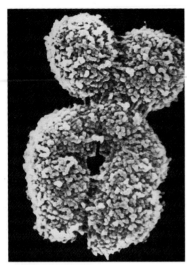

Figure 5.1 False-colour photomicrograph of human chromosome

The protein component of a chromosome consists of:
- histones
- scaffold protein
- polymerases.

The **histone** proteins have large numbers of positively charged amino groups and are referred to as basic proteins. The phosphate groups of the DNA are negatively charged and bind to the amino groups of the histones, forming a stable structure. The complex formed between the DNA and the histones is called chromatin, which exists as fibres 11 nm wide. In prepared slides of plant and animal tissues the chromatin takes up stains, enabling the nuclei of cells to become visible. Unless nuclear division is occurring, individual chromosomes will not be visible under the light microscope, but electron microscopy shows the chromatin as having a beaded appearance due to the presence of nucleosomes. Each nucleosome consists of a group of eight histone molecules (called an octamer) around which is wrapped a length of the DNA (Figure 5.2). There are 146 base pairs in the DNA around the nucleosome and this length of the double helix appears to be held in place by another histone molecule attached to the outside. The nucleosome is considered to be the basic unit in the structure of chromatin.

The nucleosome fibre is tightly coiled and this in its turn is thought to be coiled and looped around non-histone proteins collectively referred to as **scaffold** protein. Precise details of this further coiling and folding are not known.

The DNA of prokaryotic cells is not associated with proteins. The double helix of DNA is twisted and sealed, forming a circular shape.

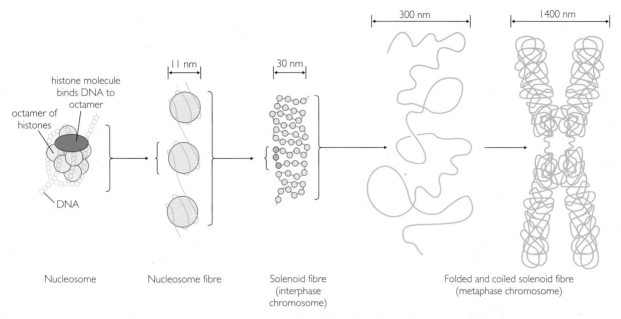

Figure 5.2 Structure of nucleosome and arrangement required to fold and coil 5 cm of DNA into a single chromosome less than 1.5 micrometres wide

The polymerases are enzymes involved with **transcription** of the genetic information during protein synthesis and with **replication** of the DNA prior to division of the chromosomes.

When it was understood that nucleic acid, rather than protein was the molecule of inheritance there was great interest in working out its composition and three-dimensional structure. James Watson and Francis Crick, working in Cambridge in 1953, were the first to show how the polynucleotide chains were arranged in the double helix of DNA. Much of the evidence was provided by Maurice Wilkins and Rosalind Franklin, of King's College, London. They passed X-rays through crystalline DNA and looked at the way in which the X-rays are scattered by the atoms in the molecule (Figure 5.3). These X-ray diffraction patterns were interpreted by Watson and Crick, who then built a model to represent DNA.

The structure of the DNA molecule is described in Chapter 2, but it is relevant here to summarise its main features in the light of its suitability for carrying genetic information:

- it is a double helix composed of two polynucleotide chains
- each polynucleotide chain has a sugar–phosphate backbone on the outside with the bases on the inside
- hydrogen bonding occurs between specific bases on opposite chains forming base pairs, holding the two chains together
- adenine (a purine) only pairs with thymine (a pyrimidine)
- guanine (a purine) only pairs with cytosine (a pyrimidine)
- the two chains are complementary; the sequence of nucleotides in one chain determines the sequence of nucleotides in the other chain
- the chains are **anti-parallel**, that is, the 3′ end of one chain lies next to the 5′ end of the other.

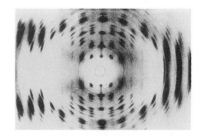

Figure 5.3 X-ray diffraction photograph (top) of DNA taken by Maurice Wilkins, which helped Francis Crick and James Watson deduce the double-helix structure of DNA and model it (above)

57

CHROMOSOMES AND THE GENETIC CODE

Replication of DNA

A molecule capable of acting as the genetic material must have a means of coding for and storing the information. In addition, it must be able to make exact copies of itself. In DNA, the nucleotides can be arranged in any sequence along one of the polynucleotide chains, so there is enormous scope for variations in their arrangement and it is possible for all the necessary information to be coded for. The complementary base pairing means that self-replication is possible and that identical copies can be made.

When Watson and Crick built their model of DNA, they suggested how replication might occur and subsequent experimental work with bacterial DNA by Kornberg and by Meselson and Stahl, provided evidence to support their hypothesis. It was suggested that the two polynucleotide chains of the DNA double helix unwind from one another, due to the disruption of the hydrogen bonds between the base pairs. Each chain then serves as a template for the synthesis of a new complementary polynucleotide chain. It was suggested that the DNA molecule 'unzips' from one end and new nucleotides, present in the nucleus, are assembled in the correct sequence according to the rules of base pairing. This is a complex process and a number of enzymes are required to catalyse the different stages. The enzyme DNA polymerase catalyses polymerisation of the polynucleotide chains, but can only work when the chain is built up in the 5′ to 3′ direction; it cannot catalyse polymerisation in the 3′ to 5′ direction. The 3′ to 5′ chain is replicated in short sections, which are then joined together by another enzyme, DNA ligase. On completion of this process along the length of the molecule, two identical 'daughter' molecules are formed, each being an exact copy of the original double helix (Figure 5.4).

This form of replication has been referred to as semi-conservative replication, because each newly formed double helix contains one of the polynucleotide chains of the original double helix.

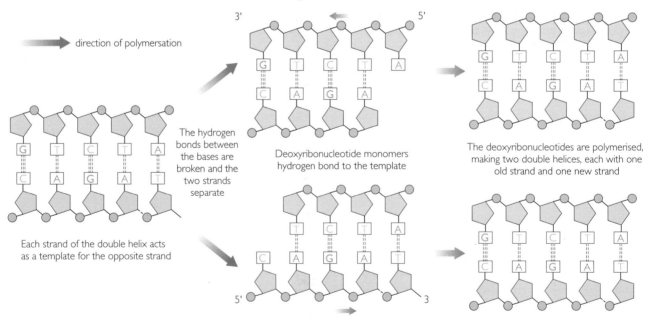

direction of polymersation

The hydrogen bonds between the bases are broken and the two strands separate

Each strand of the double helix acts as a template for the opposite strand

Deoxyribonucleotide monomers hydrogen bond to the template

The deoxyribonucleotides are polymerised, making two double helices, each with one old strand and one new strand

Figure 5.4 Stages in the semi-conservative replication of DNA, in which each polynucleotide strand acts as a template for the synthesis of a new strand

As the DNA in each chromosome is so long, replication that starts at one end and proceeds along the length of the molecule would take too much time. Observations made during the replication of *Drosophila* chromosomes have shown that the double helix opens up at a number of different sites, known as **replication forks**, thus speeding up the process.

The genetic code

A **gene** is a small section of DNA and each chromosome contains thousands of genes. As the only parts of the nucleotides making up the DNA that vary are the bases, then the information must be coded for by the type and sequence of the different nucleotide bases along the polynucleotide chains.

In the early 1900s, Sir Archibald Garrod suggested that genes exert their effects by means of enzymes. His observations on the inheritance and causes of two human diseases, alkaptonuria and phenylketonuria (PKU), led him to the idea that these conditions are due to the inability of the body to synthesise particular enzymes. In PKU the body cannot convert the amino acid phenylalanine into tyrosine, due to the absence of a single enzyme. This condition can be inherited as a recessive character determined by one gene and suggests a link between genes and enzymes.

Much later, in the 1940s, Beadle and Tatum attempted to find out how much information is contained in a single gene. They designed an experiment to test the hypothesis that one gene codes for one protein. They chose to use the bread mould, *Neurospora crassa*, for a number of reasons. It could be easily cultured in the laboratory, crosses could be made between different strains, single spores were not difficult to isolate and the results could be observed within a short time. This mould will normally grow on a solution containing a carbon source (sucrose), a nitrogen source (ammonium or nitrate ions), other mineral ions and the vitamin biotin. This solution was referred to as the minimal medium. The mould is able to produce the enzymes necessary to synthesise all the amino acids it requires. They found occasionally that a spore would be produced that was unable to grow and produce a mycelium on the minimal medium, but would grow and reproduce if provided with amino acids

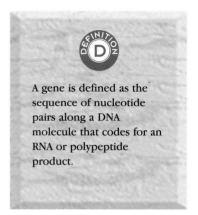

A gene is defined as the sequence of nucleotide pairs along a DNA molecule that codes for an RNA or polypeptide product.

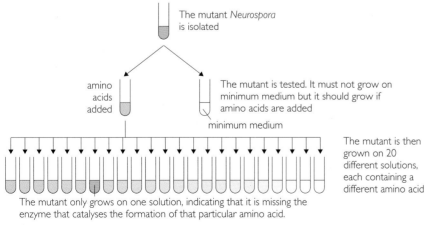

Figure 5.5 Beadle and Tatum's Neurospora *experiment, which showed that a mutation in one gene was sufficient to change the organism's ability to synthesise a particular protein*

(Figure 5.5). This appeared to be a defect in the genetic material (**a mutation**), which could be passed on to the offspring produced from the reproductive structures on the mycelium derived from the mutant spore. The mutation was shown to be due to a single faulty gene. Beadle and Tatum showed that mutant moulds of this type, incapable of growth on the minimal medium, needed only a single amino acid to be added in order to grow and reproduce normally. They concluded that the mutant was unable to synthesise an enzyme needed in the production of that particular amino acid and proposed that one gene contains the information needed for the production of a single enzyme: the **one gene – one enzyme** hypothesis. As enzymes are proteins, this hypothesis was widened to the **one gene – one protein** hypothesis.

As we realise from studies of their structure, many proteins consist of more than one polypeptide chain. A further modification of the hypothesis to take account of this was suggested by Ingram in 1956. He investigated the structure of an abnormal form of haemoglobin found in people suffering from the disorder known as sickle-cell anaemia, in which the red blood cells assume a characteristic sickle shape and do not transport oxygen as well as normal red blood cells. This condition is known to be genetically determined.

Haemoglobin molecules have four polypeptide chains: two identical α-chains and two identical β-chains. These two different polypeptides are coded for by two separate genes. Ingram showed that the difference between the normal haemoglobin and the abnormal form, known as haemoglobin S, was due to one amino acid. In the β-chains, the amino acid valine had been substituted for the amino acid glutamic acid. This evidence provided strong support for a **one gene – one polypeptide** hypothesis.

More recently, the region of DNA that carries information for the production of a polypeptide has been defined as a **cistron**. The hypothesis has been further modified to take account of this new definition and is now referred to as the **one cistron – one polypeptide** hypothesis.

As the nature of a protein is determined by the specific sequence of amino acids in the polypeptide chain, it seemed logical to suggest that the order of the nucleotides in the DNA determines the order in which the amino acids are arranged in a polypeptide. This relationship between the DNA nucleotide bases and amino acids is known as the **genetic code**. As there are twenty common amino acids and only four different nucleotide bases, it was obvious that more than one nucleotide base would have to be involved in coding for an amino acid. A code consisting of two bases for each amino acid would only cater for 16 amino acids, but if the code was three bases (**a triplet**), then there would be 64 possible combinations, more than enough for the twenty amino acids. This is known as the **base triplet hypothesis** is now accepted and the triplets are called **codons**.

Evidence for this triplet code was provided from the results of some experiments carried out by Francis Crick in 1961. He produced mutations in specific genes on viral nucleic acids by adding or removing one or more nucleotides. This type of mutation is known as a **frame shift** and changes the

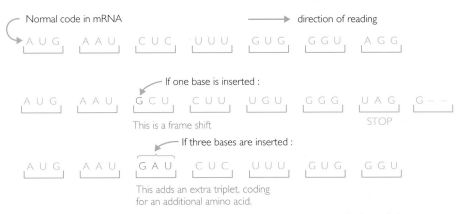

Figure 5.6 Crick's experiment on frame shift mutations in viruses, which showed that a change in one or more DNA bases in a triplet of three – a codon – resulted in a change to the proteins produced by the host cell

nature of the codons, resulting in an alteration to the amino acid sequence. If only one or two nucleotides were involved, the resulting polypeptides were abnormal, with completely different amino acids, and the chains were often shorter than the original ones. If groups of three nucleotides were involved, the polypeptides produced were almost normal as there was little change in the amino acid sequence. If a group of three nucleotides was added, there would be an extra amino acid in the polypeptide chain and if a group of three was removed there would be one amino acid less (Figure 5.6). These experiments also showed that the code was non-overlapping, that is, the bases in a specific triplet do not contribute to any adjacent triplets.

Deciphering the code

A series of experiments designed by Nirenberg in the late 1950s resulted in the discovery of the triplet bases that coded for the different amino acids. Nirenberg synthesised molecules of messenger RNA, the molecule that carries the information from the nucleus to the ribosomes in the cytoplasm. These synthetic mRNA molecules consisted of the same triplet of bases repeated many times. Twenty tubes were prepared, each containing a different radioactively labelled amino acid, together with ribosomes, enzymes, ATP and other molecules necessary for protein synthesis. Molecules of the specially synthesised mRNA were then added to each of the tubes and, after a period of time, examined to see if a polypeptide had formed. The first synthetic mRNA molecule he used consisted of UUU triplets and resulted in polypeptide formation in the tube containing the amino acid phenylalanine. Having discovered the codon for this amino acid, the codons for all the amino acids were worked out by trying different combinations of bases in the triplets. As there are 64 possible combinations of bases in the code, some amino acids are coded for by more than one codon, and there are codons that have been found to occur at the ends of polypeptide chains, the so-called chain-terminating or 'stop' codons. Because the number of codons is greater than the number of amino acids, the code is said to be **degenerate**.

For many years the genetic code was believed to be universal, with the same codons specifiying the same amino acids in all living organisms. Recent studies involving DNA-sequencing techniques have shown that the genetic codes of mitochondrial DNA are slightly different from the standard genetic code. As an example, in mammalian mitochondria, UGA specifies tryptophan rather than 'stop'. The standard genetic code, although very widely used, is not universal.

Protein synthesis

Protein synthesis involves the transfer of the coded information from the nucleus to the cytoplasm (**transcription**) and the conversion of that information into polypeptides on the ribosomes (**translation**). Both these stages involve another nucleic acid, ribonucleic acid (RNA), which is present in abundance in cells that are synthesising proteins.

Ribonucleic acid is similar in structure to DNA, in that each is a polynucleotide, but it differs in that:
- it is a single-stranded molecule
- it contains the pentose ribose instead of deoxyribose
- the base thymine is replaced by uracil.

There are three different types of RNA present in cells and they are all involved in some way with the synthesis of proteins. They are:
- messenger RNA (mRNA), which is formed in the nucleus during the process of transcription and which carries the instructions from the DNA to the ribosomes
- ribosomal RNA (rRNA), which is a component of the ribosomes on which the polypeptide chains are built up
- transfer RNA (tRNA), which is present in the cytoplasm and which picks up amino acids and transports them to the ribosomes for assembly into polypeptides.

Transcription

Transcription occurs in the nucleus. The enzyme RNA-polymerase becomes attached to the double helix of the DNA, in the region of the gene that is being expressed. This usually occurs at a codon for the amino acid methionine, which acts as a 'start' signal. The hydrogen bonds in this region of the double helix are broken and the DNA unwinds. One of the strands of the DNA, the coding

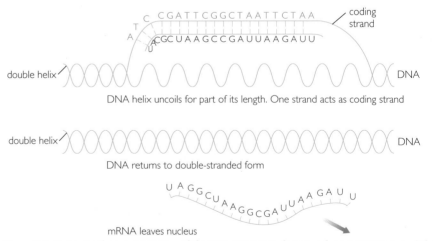

Figure 5.7 Stages in the transcription of the DNA genetic code to produce a mRNA strand that leaves the nucleus for translation in the cytoplasm

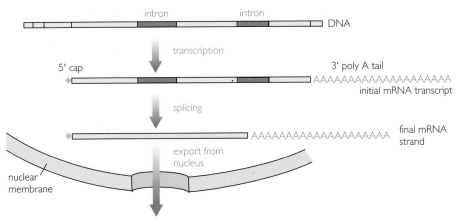

Figure 5.8 Stages in the removal of non-coding lengths of DNA – introns – from the original DNA strand, leading to export of the mature mRNA from the nucleus

strand, acts as a template and is copied by base pairing of nucleotides. A complementary polynucleotide strand of messenger RNA is built up from a pool of nucleotides in the nucleus (Figure 5.7). The formation of the strand is catalysed by RNA-polymerase. As it forms, the strand of mRNA detaches from the coding strand of the DNA and, when complete, it leaves the nucleus through a pore in the nuclear envelope. Once in the cytoplasm, it becomes attached to a ribosome.

Before the mRNA leaves the nucleus, it is modified by the addition of a guanine molecule to the 5′ end of the polynucleotide chain. This is referred to as a 'cap' and is thought to act as a signal promoting translation, once the mRNA reaches a ribosome. At the 3′ end of the chain, a 'tail' of about a hundred adenine nucleotides is added, called poly-A. It is suggested that this tail may act as a signal for the export of the mRNA from the nucleus and it is also considered to offer some protection from enzyme action, as those mRNA strands that lack such tails do not survive for long in the cytoplasm.

Eukaryotic genes contain regions that do not code for amino acids. These non-coding regions are called **introns** and are copied from the DNA along with the coding regions, or exons, during transcription. After the 5′ cap and the 3′ tail have been added to the mRNA, and before it leaves the nucleus, the introns are removed by enzyme action (Figure 5.8). The exons are then joined up, so that the mRNA that leaves the nucleus consists of a continuous coding region. The function of the introns is not known.

Translation

Translation occurs on the ribosomes in the cytoplasm. The mRNA binds to the small sub-unit of a ribosome and is held in such a way that its codons are exposed. These codons need to be recognised and pair with complementary **anticodons** on the transfer RNA molecules.

All transfer RNA molecules have the same basic structure. Each consists of a single polynucleotide strand of RNA, about 80 bases long, which is bent back on itself forming a clover-leaf arrangement, held in place by some areas of base pairing. The anticodon consists of a triplet of unpaired bases on one portion of

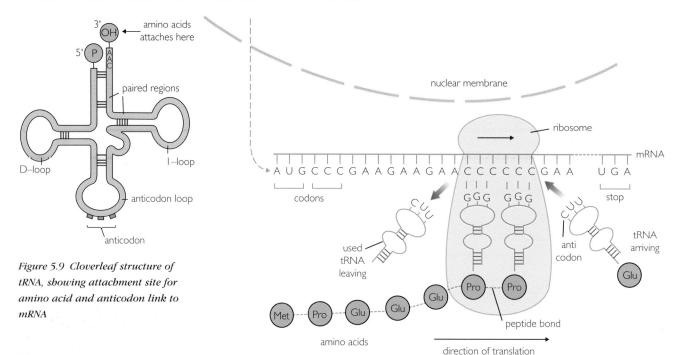

Figure 5.9 Cloverleaf structure of tRNA, showing attachment site for amino acid and anticodon link to mRNA

Figure 5.10 Stages in translation of mRNA strand on ribosomes and condensation reactions between amino acids on tRNAs, forming new polypeptide chain

the molecule. The anticodon is complementary to one or more of the codons of mRNA. At the opposite end of the molecule is a site for the attachment of a specific amino acid. The base guanine is always found at the 5′ end of the strand and the 3′ end always has the base sequence CCA.

Before becoming attached to its tRNA molecule, a specific amino acid is activated by ATP. An intermediate is formed, which then joins with the tRNA to form amino acyl-tRNA (Figure 5.9). This reaction is catalysed by an enzyme, amino-acyl tRNA synthetase.

As the ribosome moves along the mRNA strand, two tRNA molecules, with their amino acids, can be held in position at any one time. Their complementary anticodons are held in place opposite the codons on the mRNA by hydrogen bonding. An enzyme, peptidyl transferase, catalyses the formation of a peptide bond between the two amino acids. As the bond is formed, the ribosome moves one triplet further along the mRNA strand (Figure 5.10). Once the amino acids have joined, the tRNA molecules are released and can form a complex with another amino acid of the same type.

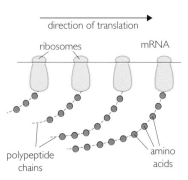

Figure 5.11 A polysome, or polyribosome, is a group of ribosomes translating the same mRNA strand at different points, generating a large number of copies of the polypeptide

Amino acids can be joined to the growing polypeptide chain at the rate of 15 per second. The base pairing between the codons on the mRNA and the anticodons on the tRNA molecules ensures that the transcribed information on the mRNA is exactly translated into the correct sequence of amino acids in the polypeptide chain. Each polypeptide chain usually begins with the amino acid methionine, which is coded TAC on the DNA, giving the codon AUG on the mRNA. The anticodon UAC on the tRNA brings the correct amino acid to the ribosome to start the chain. The sequence is completed when the ribosome reaches a 'stop' codon (UAA, UGA or UAG). On completion, the polypeptide leaves the ribosome. It is not yet a protein, as it has to acquire its secondary structure, coiling into an α-helix or arrangement into a β-pleated sheet, and further folding to form its tertiary structure.

Several ribosomes can attach to an mRNA strand simultaneously, forming **polysomes**, speeding up polypeptide chain formation (Figure 5.11). It has been observed that ribosomes can initiate protein synthesis many times on the same mRNA strand, so that a great deal of protein can be produced from one mRNA molecule.

Ribosomes occur both freely in the cytoplasm and attached to the endoplasmic reticulum. Proteins that are destined for secretion are synthesised on the ribosomes attached to the ER and have special signal sequences, which interact with the membrane of the ER. When the polypeptide chains are released from the ribosomes, they pass through the membrane of the ER and are transported in vesicles to the Golgi apparatus, where they may be modified. Vesicles formed from the Golgi apparatus then transport the proteins to the cell surface membrane, where exocytosis occurs and the protein is secreted from the cell.

Although reference has been made in this chapter to specific amino acids, their codons and anticodons, it is not necessary for these names to be remembered.

Structural and regulatory genes

There are two main types of genes that code for polypeptides:
- structural genes, which code for functional proteins such as enzymes, hormones, antibodies, storage proteins and fibres
- regulatory genes, which control the activities of other genes.

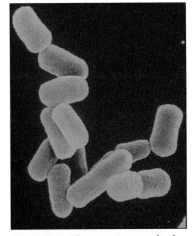

Figure 5.12 Electronmicrograph of the gut bacterium Escherichia coli, *used by Jacob and Monod in their studies of structural and regulatory genes*

All the body cells of an organism contain the same genetic information. They have the same number of chromosomes with the same number of genes, so it is logical to suggest that there is some mechanism by which the activity of genes is controlled. In the early 1950s, Jacob and Monod designed a series of experiments to investigate how enzyme synthesis was controlled in the gut bacterium *Escherichia coli* (Figure 5.12). It was known that some enzymes were produced all the time, but others were only synthesised if a particular compound was present. Jacob and Monod found that *E. coli* would grow well if supplied with glucose, but if supplied with lactose growth would stop for a short time, after which it would grow rapidly again. Their investigations showed that in order to break down the lactose, the bacterium needed to synthesise other enzymes that were not normally present. In 1961 they suggested that the structural genes coding for these enzymes were present on the DNA, but their transcription and translation were suppressed by a regulator gene. The regulator gene codes for a so-called repressor molecule, which binds to part of the DNA, preventing the intitiation of transcription of the codons for the enzymes that enable the bacterium to take up and metabolise lactose. When lactose is present, it binds to the repressor molecule and inactivates it. As soon as the lactose is removed or used up, synthesis of the enzymes ceases within a short time. Jacob and Monod mapped the location of these genes on the bacterial DNA and found that they were side-by-side and close to two other

CHROMOSOMES AND THE GENETIC CODE

Operon repressed: lactose absent, genes 'switched off'

Operon induced: lactose present, genes 'switched on'

Figure 5.13 Jacob and Monod proposed that, in the absence of lactose, a repressor protein blocks transcription of the genes that code for the production of enzymes needed to metabolise lactose. If lactose is present it binds to the repressor and the genes that lead to enzyme production are 'switched on'

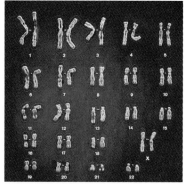

Figure 5.14 Photomicrograph of complete set of 46 human chromosomes from a somatic (body) cell, arranged in 23 similar (homologous) pairs.

The diploid number is defined as the number of chromosomes found in the zygote, resulting from the fusion of two haploid gametes, and in all the body (or somatic) cells derived from it.

regions, called the **promoter** and **operator regions**, which are also involved in the control mechanism. The mechanism is shown in Figure 5.13.

Jacob and Monod called the length of DNA which consists of the structural genes for the lactose breakdown, together with the promoter and operator regions, an **operon**. Several other operons have been described for bacteria, but no such mechanisms have been found in eukaryotes. In bacteria, transcription and translation are more closely linked than they are in a eukaryote, where transcription occurs in the nucleus and translation in the cytoplasm.

Transfer and ribosomal RNA

Transfer and ribosomal RNA molecules are also coded for by genes, but they are not synthesised in the same way as proteins. They are made directly by transcription from the DNA in the nucleus, in much the same way as messenger RNA is built up. The genes that code for rRNA, of which there are three different types, are present in multiple copies found in special regions of a chromosome. These regions are called **secondary constrictions**, or nucleolar organisers.

Nuclear division

Chromosome number

The number of chromosomes present in the cells of an individual organism is usually constant and will be the same for all other individuals of the same species, but the cells of individuals of different species will have a different

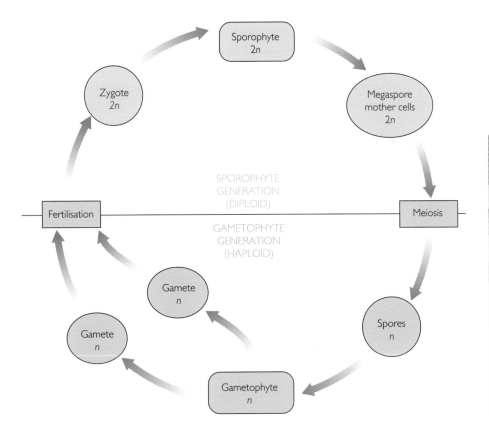

Figure 5.15 *Alternation of haploid and diploid generations commonly occurs in mosses and ferns. Fertilisation of haploid gametes produces a diploid sporophyte generation, which releases haploid spores that grow into the gametophyte plant*

number. For example, onion cells have 16 chromosomes, tomatoes have 24 and humans have 46 (Figure 5.14). This number is referred to as the chromosome number of the species. The chromosomes are seen to be in pairs, that is, there are two identical sets of chromosomes in each cell, so the chromosome number is said to be **diploid**. It is written as 2n, so for the onion 2n = 16, for tomatoes 2n = 24 and for humans 2n = 46. It follows that the gametes will normally contain only one of each pair of chromosomes, that is a single set. They are described as **haploid** and the number is written as n. In the examples we have chosen, the haploid numbers are n = 8 for the onion, n = 12 for tomatoes and n = 23 for humans.

In the case of organisms known as polyploids, which have more than two sets of chromosomes, it is more usual to refer to the basic number of different chromosomes in a single haploid set as x. In diploid organisms, the number of chromosomes in the gametes (n) is the same as the basic number (x), so n = x. Using humans as an example, x = 23 and 2n = 2x = 46. This is usually abbreviated to 2n = 46, but when it is known that an organism is polyploid it is more correct to represent the chromosome number using both n and x. The cultivated bread wheat *Triticum aestivum* is known to be a hexaploid, with

Figure 5.16 *In flowering plants the sporophyte is dominant*

42 chromosomes; x = 7, so its chromosome number is written 2n = 6x = 42. Members of the plant kingdom have a life cycle that involves the alternation of a haploid (n) generation (**gametophyte**), on which gametes are produced, with a diploid (2n) generation (**sporophyte**) producing spores (Figure 5.15). This **alternation of generations** is very obvious in the mosses and ferns, but less noticeable in the flowering plants, where the sporophyte is dominant and the gametophyte generation reduced to a few cells.

Mitosis and meiosis

The information held on the chromosomes in the nucleus is used to manufacture cell components and to control the metabolic activities of cells through the production of enzymes and hormones. It is essential that this information is passed on to new cells produced within an organism and to new individuals produced as a result of sexual reproduction. Two types of nuclear division occur:

- **mitosis**, which results in two, genetically identical daughter nuclei containing the same number of chromosomes as the nucleus of the parent cell
- **meiosis**, where four daughter nuclei are produced, each having half the number of chromosomes contained in the original parent nucleus.

Mitosis is usually followed by the division of the cytoplasm into equal portions around each daughter nucleus, a process known as **cytokinesis**. This type of division results in an increase in the numbers of cells and is associated with the growth of an individual organism, or a colony if the organism is unicellular. In addition, it is found where repair and replacement of tissues occurs, such as in the formation of callus tissue where wounding has occurred in flowering plants, and in the replacement of red blood cells in vertebrates. In the life cycles of prokaryotes, protoctists and fungi, it is associated with asexual reproduction. The essential features of mitosis are that the chromosome number is maintained and that there is no change in the genetic information. If a diploid nucleus undergoes mitosis, the daughter nuclei are diploid (2n → 2n)

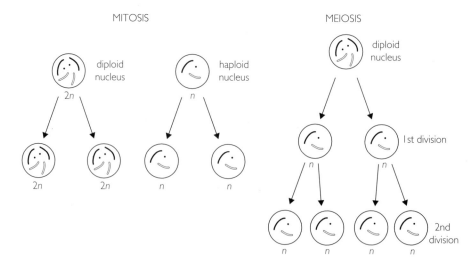

Figure 5.17 Summary of the events in mitosis and meiosis, showing that mitosis replicates the parent condition, whether diploid (2n) or haploid (n), whereas meiosis halves the number of chromosomes, producing the haploid number

and if the parent nucleus is haploid, the daughter nuclei are haploid (n → n). Meiosis is often referred to as a reduction division, because it results in daughter nuclei with the haploid number of chromosomes from a parent nucleus that is diploid. It occurs during gamete formation in animals and during spore formation in plants that have an alternation of generations. It is of great significance since it enables the chromosome number of the species to remain constant, the diploid number being restored when two gametes fuse during fertilisation. Meiosis introduces the possibility of genetic variation, due to some of the events that take place during the first stage of the division.

The events of mitosis and meiosis are summarised in Figure 5.17.

As stated earlier in this chapter, it is only when the nuclei of cells are about to undergo division that the chromosomes become visible in stained preparations of tissues viewed under the light microscope. Prior to both mitosis and meiosis, the DNA replicates, so that each chromosome consists of two identical polynucleotide chains. The chromosomes appear as double structures: two strands called **chromatids**, lying side by side, attached to each other at a region called the **centromere** (Figure 5.18).

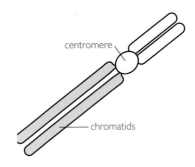

Figure 5.18 Structure of a chromosome showing identical 'sister' chromatids and the centromere, a connecting point essential to chromosome separation during cell division

The cell cycle

The sequence of events that occurs from the formation of an individual cell until it divides to form daughter cells is called the cell cycle. It is usual to divide the cycle into three stages:
- interphase
- mitosis
- division of cytoplasm (cytokinesis).

Interphase

Observations of nuclei in prepared tissue sections reveal very little taking place during interphase. The nucleus appears as a spherical structure surrounded by a nuclear envelope. The chromatin takes up stains and shows as a granular network in which there are one or more darker staining areas, the **nucleoli**. The nucleoli are not surrounded by a membrane and consist of areas of protein and rRNA. During this stage, which is the longest in the cell cycle, three distinct phases can be distinguished. In the first, shown as G1 in Figure 5.19, the cell is undergoing a period of rapid growth. New organelles are being synthesised, so the cell requires both structural proteins and enzymes, resulting in a great amount of protein synthesis. The metabolic rate of the cell will be high. This phase is followed by the synthesis of new DNA in the nucleus, shown as S on the diagram. Histones, the proteins to which the DNA is linked, are built up and each chromosome becomes divided into two chromatids. In the third phase, G2, more cell growth takes place, some of the cell organelles divide, there is an accumulation of energy stores and the chromosomes begin the process of condensation prior to their division.

Mitosis

Interphase is followed by mitosis, the nuclear division that involves the separation of sister chromatids and their distribution into the daughter nuclei. The events that take place during this separation are continuous, but for

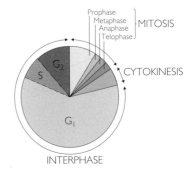

Figure 5.19 The cell cycle, showing the relative durations of the stages in chromosome duplication and separation (mitosis) and cell division (cytokinesis)

CHROMOSOMES AND THE GENETIC CODE

Figure 5.20 Photomicrograph of cell division spindle formation in sea urchin eggs

descriptive purposes it has been convenient to recognise four main stages: **prophase**, **metaphase**, **anaphase** and **telophase**. Overall, the process involves condensation of the chromosomes and their precise arrangement in the cell so that, when the chromatids are pulled apart, they are divided exactly into two identical groups (see Practical: Preparation of a root tip squash).

In prophase, the chromosomes first appear as long tangled threads that gradually become shorter and thicker, due to spiralisation. Eventually they are seen to consist of two chromatids, which are held together at an unstained region called the centromere. The nucleoli get smaller and gradually disappear. In most animal and some plant cells, the **centrioles**, situated just outside the nuclear envelope in the cytoplasm, move to opposite ends (poles) of the cell. **Microtubules** radiate out from the centrioles, forming an aster. When all these events have taken place, the nuclear envelope breaks up and microtubules are organised to form a barrel-shaped structure, called a **spindle**, across the central part of the cell, between the centrioles. The microtubules involved in the spindle are referred to as **spindle fibres**.

During metaphase, the chromosomes become attached to the spindle fibres by their centromeres. They move up and down so that they are aligned along the central part, or equator, of the spindle. They are arranged at right angles to the axis of the spindle and the sister chromatids of each chromosome are easily distinguished.

The centromeres divide and the spindle fibres shorten, pulling the centromeres to opposite poles. This is anaphase and results in the separation of the chromatids.

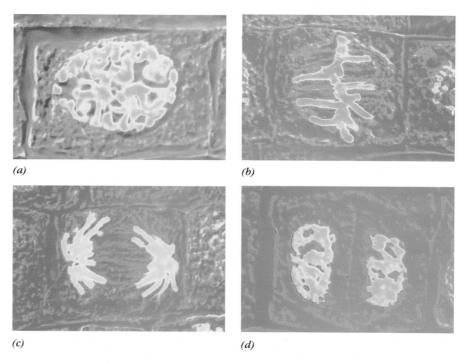

(a)

(b)

(c)

(d)

Figure 5.21 Photomicrographs of mitosis in Hyacinth root tip cells, showing the four main phases of division – (a) prophase, (b) metaphase, (c) anaphase and (d) telophase

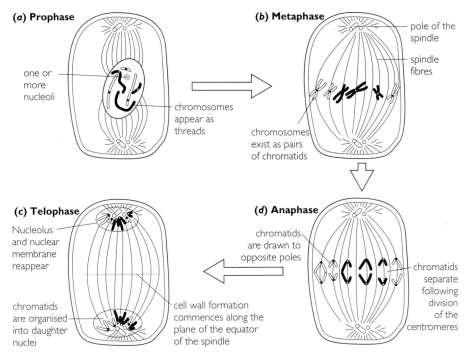

(a) **Prophase**

one or more nucleoli

chromosomes appear as threads

(b) **Metaphase**

pole of the spindle

spindle fibres

chromosomes exist as pairs of chromatids

(c) **Telophase**

Nucleolus and nuclear membrane reappear

chromatids are organised into daughter nuclei

cell wall formation commences along the plane of the equator of the spindle

(d) **Anaphase**

chromatids are drawn to opposite poles

chromatids separate following division of the centromeres

Figure 5.22 *Diagrammatic representations of the four phases of mitosis – (a) prophase, (b) metaphase, (c) anaphase and (d) telophase*

Once separated, the chromatids are now referred to as daughter chromosomes. When they reach the poles of the cell, at telophase, they begin to lengthen, uncoiling and losing their visibility. A nuclear envelope forms around each group of daughter chromosomes, nucleoli reappear and the division of the nucleus is completed (Figures 5.21, 5.22).

Cytokinesis

Cytokinesis follows telophase. The other cell organelles, such as ribosomes and mitochondria, become evenly distributed around each nucleus and the process of division of the cytoplasm begins. In animal cells, the process is sometimes referred to as **cleavage**, since a furrow develops by intucking of the cell surface membrane. It is thought that protein fibres in the cytoplasm, called **microfilaments**, are involved. The furrow becomes deeper until eventually the two cells separate.

In plant cells, the spindle fibres in the equator region of the cell do not disappear but move outwards, forming a structure known as a **phragmoplast**. Many cell organelles congregate in this area and a number of fluid-filled vesicles are budded off from the Golgi apparatus. These vesicles contain material that is needed to build a middle lamella and a new cellulose cell wall. The vesicles join up together to form the **cell plate**, which grows across the middle, eventually separating the two daughter cells (Figure 5.23). The membranes of the vesicles contribute to the new cell surface membranes. In certain regions, the vesicles do not fuse, leaving a cytoplasmic connection called a **plasmodesma** (plural: **plasmodesmata**) between the two daughter cells.

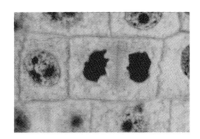

Figure 5.23 *Photomicrograph of cleavage and cell-plate formation in dividing onion* (Allium) *root tip cells*

Meiosis

Before considering the process of meiosis, it is helpful to understand the origin and nature of the chromosomes in a diploid cell. In a diploid organism, one set of chromosomes will have come from the male parent and the other set from the female parent, so that the chromosomes occur in pairs in the cells. These pairs of chromosomes are called homologous pairs.

The members of a pair have the following characteristics:
• they are exactly the same length
• they have the centromere in the same position
• they contain the same number of genes
• the genes are arranged in the same linear order.

When mitosis occurs, the homologous chromosomes act independently, but in meiosis, pairing of homologous chromosomes takes place during the first stage, prophase I, and their subsequent separation ensures that one of each pair is present in the gametes or spores that are formed.

Meiosis differs from mitosis in that it involves a reduction in the number of chromosomes from the diploid number (2n) to the haploid number (n). Replication of the DNA takes place in interphase, but this is followed by two cycles of nuclear division, one in which separation of homologous chromosomes occurs and the other where the chromatids are separated. These are usually referred to as the first and second meiotic divisions and result in the production of four haploid nuclei from one diploid nucleus. This type of nuclear division occurs during **gametogenesis** (the production of sperm and ova) in animals and in spore formation in the sporophyte generations of plants. As mentioned earlier, the gametes will have a single set of chromosomes, but these will not be identical. During prophase I, when the chromosomes pair up, there is the possibility of exchange of sections of non-sister chromatids, leading to variation.

The events that take place during meiosis form a continuous process, but, as with mitosis, they are separated into different stages for ease of description. The same stages occur, but as there are two divisions of the nucleus, each stage occurs twice (see Practical: Meiosis in pollen mother cells). For example, prophase I refers to the first meiotic division and prophase II to prophase in the second meiotic division.

Prophase I

In prophase I, the chromosomes become visible as single threads. It is not possible to distinguish their double structure in the early stages, but initially each chromosome appears to have a beaded appearance due to localised coiling of the DNA, forming regions called **chromomeres**. Homologous chromosomes pair up precisely along their length, process known as **synapsis**, and more condensation makes them appear shorter and fatter. Each pair of chromosomes is called a **bivalent**. As the chromatids of each homologous chromosome become visible, the members of a pair seem to repel each other in some regions but remain attracted at others. At the points of attraction, non-sister chromatids break and rejoin at exactly corresponding locations. This is

Figure 5.24 Photomicrograph of prophase I of meiosis in Lillium, *showing the chromosomes as threads, with some regions of contact between chromatids*

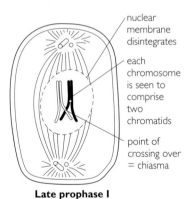

nuclear membrane disintegrates

each chromosome is seen to comprise two chromatids

point of crossing over = chiasma

Late prophase I

Figure 5.25 Diagrammatic representation of prophase I of meiosis, showing that the regions of contact between chromatids (chiasmata) are points where genetic material crosses over when the chromatids break and rejoin

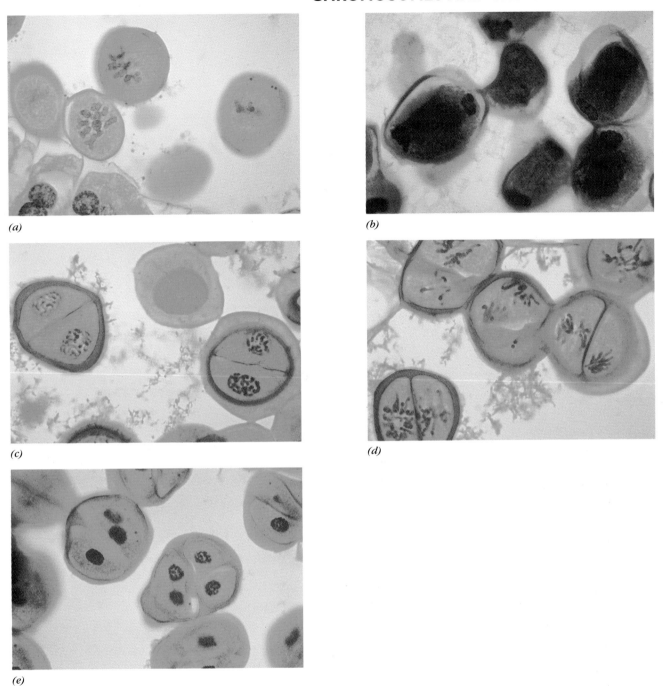

Figure 5.26 Photomicrographs of meiosis in Lilium *pollen mother cells, showing the remaining phases of division to form haploid cells – (a) metaphase I, (b) late anaphase I in which the cytoplasm becomes very dense and (c) telophase I and first cell cleavage, followed by (d) metaphase II and anaphase II in different cells, and (e) telophase II and second cell cleavage*

known as **crossing over** and results in the formation of **chiasmata** (sing. **chiasma**, from the Greek for 'cross arrangement'). More than one chiasma can form and it may involve the same pair or another pair of non-sister chromatids. If one chiasma forms, the bivalents have a cross shape, if two a ring shape and if more than two a series of loops arise at right angles to each other. Chiasmata hold the two homologous chromosomes together and this leads to their

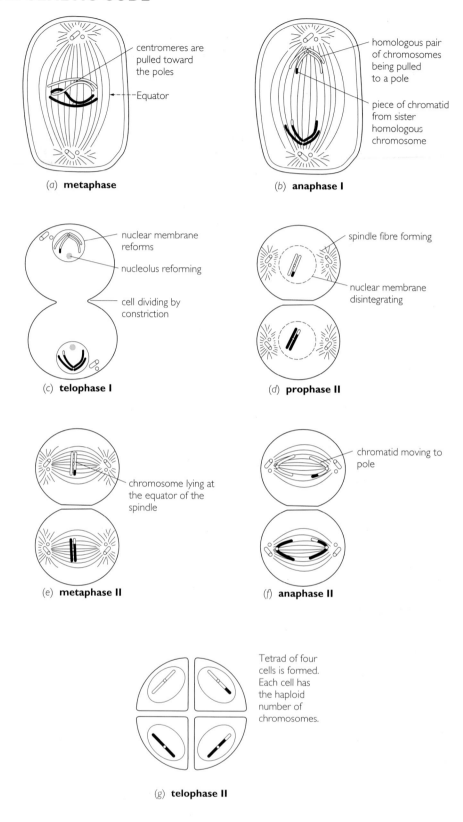

Figure 5.27 *Diagrammatic representations of the remaining phases of meiotic division to form haploid cells: (a) metaphase I, (b) anaphase I and (c) telophase I, followed by (d) prophase II, (e) metaphase II, (f) anaphase II and (g) telophase II*

orderly separation during anaphase I. During the later stages of prophase I, the nucleoli disappear, the centrioles migrate to opposite poles of the cell and the nuclear envelope breaks down. Spindle formation begins as microtubules become arranged across the middle of the cell from pole to pole (Figures 5.24, 5.25).

Metaphase I

The bivalents become attached to the spindle in metaphase I (Figures 5.26a, 5.27a). The centromeres attach to individual spindle fibres and the bivalents are moved so that they are arranged along the equator of the spindle. They are orientated so that the centromere of one homologous chromosome will move to one pole and the other will move to the opposite pole. At this point, the centromeres of each homologous pair repel each other strongly, but the sister chromatids are closely associated.

Anaphase I

In anaphase I, the homologous chromosomes are separated (Figures 5.26b, 5.27b). The centromeres are pulled by the spindle fibres towards opposite poles. The attraction between sister chromatids ceases. The reduction in the number of chromosomes is achieved by this separation.

Telophase I

Telophase I does not always occur, but in most animal and some plant cells, the chromatids begin to uncoil and a nuclear envelope forms around each group of chromatids (Figures 5.26c, 5.27c). In many plants, this stage does not occur and the nucleus passes straight into metaphase II of the next stage of division. There may be a short interphase between the two stages, but there is no replication of the DNA.

Prophase II

There is no prophase II if interphase is lacking, as the chromosomes will already be condensed. If nucleoli and nuclear envelopes were reformed in telophase I then these will disappear and two new spindles will form at right angles to the plane of the original spindle (Figures 5.26d, 5.27d).

Metaphase II

At metaphase II, each of the chromosomes attaches by its centromere to a spindle fibre and the chromosomes are brought into line up the equators of the spindles (Figures 5.26e, 5.27e).

Anaphase II

Separation of the sister chromatids is achieved at anaphase II (Figures 5.26f, 5.27f). The centromeres divide and the chromatids, now called daughter chromosomes, are pulled by the spindle fibres to opposite poles of the spindle.

Telophase II

During telophase II, the daughter chromosomes despiralise and become less visible. The nucleoli reappear and new nuclear envelopes form around the groups of chromosomes (Figures 5.26g, 5.27g).

The first and second telophases are usually accompanied by division of the cytoplasm.

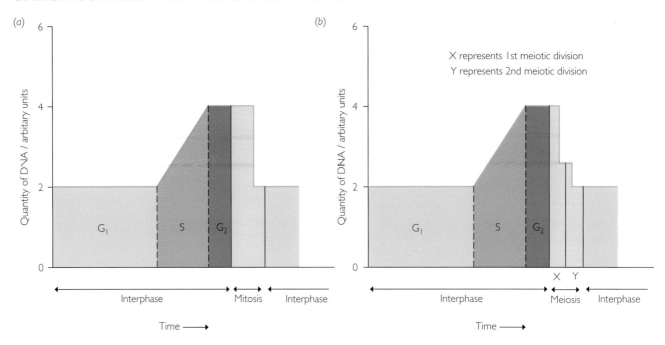

Figure 5.28 Graphs to illustrate changes in DNA content of a cell during (a) the cell cycle, and (b) meiosis. Note that, in meiosis, the DNA content of each daughter cell is only half that of the parent cell

As mentioned earlier, replication of the DNA occurs during interphase before prophase I. At that time, the DNA content of the nucleus doubles. The amount of DNA in each nucleus is half the original amount after the first stage of the meiotic division. By the end of the second meiotic division, the amount in each nucleus is halved again (Figure 5.28).

Significance of meiosis

It is significant that meiosis offers a mechanism for some genetic variation in a species, whereas mitosis maintains genetic stability. In meiosis, the separation of homologous chromosomes, resulting in the reduction of the diploid (2n) to the haploid (n) number means that each gamete or spore will only carry one form of the gene for a particular characteristic. The crossing over that occurs in prophase I, before the separation of the homologous pairs in anaphase I, results in the exchange of genetic information between maternal and paternal chromosomes, leading to the possibility of new combinations of genes in the gametes. In addition, the orientation of the bivalents on the spindle at metaphase I is completely random, so that the products of the first meiotic division will contain a mixture of chromosomes of maternal and paternal origin. Similarly, during metaphase II, orientation of the pairs of chromatids is random. All these events result in the possibility of a large number of different chromosome combinations in the gametes. This is referred to as **independent assortment of chromosomes** and makes a contribution to the way in which particular characteristics are inherited.

Mitosis and meiosis compared

There are a number of similarities between the two processes. They both involve:

- replication of the DNA in interphase
- replication of cell organelles
- similar stages of prophase, metaphase, anaphase and telophase, during which similar events take place
- formation of a spindle.

Mitosis and meiosis differ in a number of ways, which are summarised in Table 5.1.

Table 5.1 *Summary of differences between mitosis and meiosis*

Mitosis	Meiosis
consists of one division separating sister chromatids	consists of two divisions: separation of homologous chromosomes followed by separation of chromatids
homologous chromosomes do not associate	homologous chromosomes pair up
no chromomeres visible in prophase	chromomeres often visible in prophase
no crossing over occurs	crossing over occurs
no chiasmata formation	chiasmata formation
daughter nuclei have same number of chromosomes as parent nucleus	daughter nuclei have half the number of chromosomes as the parent nucleus
no genetic variation in daughter nuclei	genetic variation possible in daughter nuclei
can occur in haploid, diploid or polyploid cells	occurs in diploid and some polyploid cells
associated with increase in numbers of cells, replacement and repair, asexual reproduction and with gamete formation in the gametophyte generation of plants	associated with gametogenesis in animals and with spore production in the sporophyte generation of plants

CHROMOSOMES AND THE GENETIC CODE

Preparation of a root tip squash

Introduction

Garlic root tips provide a reliable source of actively dividing cells to demonstrate mitosis. Individual garlic cloves, supported over water using cocktail sticks, will produce numerous roots within four to five days. The demonstration of chromosomes is by the Feulgen reaction. Acid hydrolysis of DNA results in the formation of aldehydes, which react with Schiff's reagent to produce a bright red-purple colour. This method is specific for DNA.

Materials

- Actively growing garlic roots
- Fixative (99 cm^3 70 per cent aqueous industrial methylated spirits plus 1 cm^3 glacial ethanoic acid)
- 1.0 molar hydrochloric acid
- 70 per cent aqueous glycerol
- Distilled water
- Schiff's reagent
- Water bath at 60 °C
- Test tubes
- Microscope slides and coverslips
- Scalpels
- Mounted needles
- Blotting paper
- Microscope

FLAMMABLE
methylated
spirits

CORROSIVE
ethanoic
acid
hydrochloric
acid

Method

1 Cut off the end 1 cm of a root and fix in a mixture of 99 cm^3 70 per cent (aqueous) industrial methylated spirit, plus 1 cm^3 glacial ethanoic acid for at least 2 hours.

2 Treat the root tips in 1 molar hydrochloric acid at 60 °C for 6 to 7 minutes. This is the critical part of the method; if treated for longer the staining reaction becomes weaker.

3 Remove the acid and rinse thoroughly in distilled water.

4 Add Schiff's reagent and leave for one hour.

5 Rinse again in distilled water.

6 Place one root tip on a microscope slide, cut off and discard all but the darkly stained tip. Add a couple of drops of 70 per cent aqueous glycerol and, using mounted needles, break up the root tip.

7 Carefully apply a coverslip and place the slide between several sheets of blotting paper. Squash gently. The cells should now be sufficiently well spread out.

8 Examine the preparation using a microscope, first with low magnification, then high. Look carefully for cells with visible chromosomes.

Results and discussion

1 Make labelled drawings of representative stages of mitosis.

2 Count the total number of cells visible in the field of view. Then, count the total number of cells that show stages of mitosis and express this as a percentage of the total number of cells present in the field of view. This percentage is known as the mitotic index and is a measure of the proportion of the time spent in mitotic division.

Meiosis in pollen mother cells

Introduction

Tradescantia spp. provide very useful material for the demonstration of meiosis, as they give a succession of flowers from May to October. The chromosomes are large and relatively small in number. Very small buds should be selected and the anthers stained using aceto-orcein. This stain is made up by dissolving 1 g of orcein in 99 cm³ of 45 per cent (aqueous) ethanoic acid. Filter the stain after several hours to remove any undissolved residue.

Materials

CORROSIVE
aceto-orcein

- *Tradescantia* flower buds
- Fine forceps
- Aceto-orcein
- Watch glasses
- Forceps to hold watchmaker's forceps
- Bunsen burner
- Microscope slides and cover slips
- Small glass rods
- Blotting paper
- Microscope

Method

1 Use fine forceps to remove anthers from flower buds. Watchmaker's forceps are ideal.
2 Place in a watch glass containing 2 cm³ of aceto-orcein and add a couple of drops of 1.0 M hydrochloric acid.
3 Hold the watch glass firmly with forceps and warm gently over a low bunsen flame until the liquid just begins to steam. Do not allow it to boil.
4 Leave for ten minutes to take up the stain, then place the anthers on a microscope slide. Add three or four drops of fresh stain and break up the anthers using a small glass rod.
5 Carefully apply a coverslip and place the slide between several sheets of blotting paper. Squash firmly, avoiding any sideways movement.
6 Examine the preparation using a microscope, first with low magnification, then high. Look carefully for cells with visible chromosomes, which should be stained darkly.

Results and discussion

1 Make labelled drawings of representative stages of meiosis from your preparation.
2 Summarise the differences between mitosis and meiosis.
3 How does the process of meiosis contribute to genetic variation?

6 Patterns of inheritance

Genes and alleles

Genetics involves the study of heredity. It is heredity that is responsible for the similarities between parents and their offspring. When organisms reproduce, their offspring are of the same species and the members of one family are all similar to one another and to their parents in their specific characteristics. We recognise the species characteristics of humans as being different from those of rabbits and gorillas, but we also recognise that the individuals within one different species vary in small ways. These small differences constitute **variation**, which, as discussed in chapter 5, may be the result of genetic changes taking place during the formation of the gametes, or of the influence of the environment or a combination of both. In some cases it is difficult to determine what contribution is made by heredity and what is due to the environment, especially if the differences are very small. In humans, factors such as colour of the skin, hair colour, weight, shape of head and facial features all show variation and we know that many of these are inherited characteristics because we use them to distinguish between the various ethnic subgroups of our species. Some of these factors, for example weight, can be affected by the level of nutrition or exercise, which are both environmental influences.

We recognise two forms of variation:
- discontinuous
- continuous.

These two forms of variation describe differences in the appearance of the characters and do not describe the genetic differences. In **discontinuous variation**, there are clear-cut differences in the forms of the various characters. The characters in the garden pea, *Pisum sativum*, which the Austrian monk Gregor Mendel worked with when he did his experiments on inheritance, are good examples of discontinuous variation. When tall pea plants were crossed with dwarf pea plants, all the plants were tall. In subsequent generations, which had been allowed to self-pollinate, both tall and dwarf plants appeared, but there were no intermediates (Figure 6.1a). Similarly, there are polled (hornless) and horned forms of cattle, vestigial and normal-winged *Drosophila* (Figure 6.2) and yellow and purple seeds in maize. The differences between the two forms are determined by alternative forms, or **alleles**, of a single gene and no measurements are needed to distinguish between them.

Much of the variation that occurs within a species is concerned with size, mass or shape, characters that do not fall easily into groups. Such characters are usually determined by several genes, each of which has a small effect. It is difficult to measure the individual contribution of each gene, especially as the environment has a great influence on this type of variation. This variation is known as **continuous variation** and is clearly shown by height in humans (Figure 6.1b). Within a human population, there is usually a range of height in adult males from 150 cm to 190 cm. There are no separate categories but a

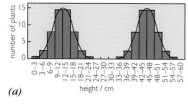

(a)

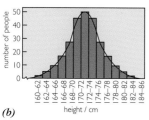

(b)

*Figure 6.1 Histograms to illustrate
(a) discontinuous variation in height
of pea plants, some of a dwarf
variety and some of a tall variety,
showing that there is no overlap in
height distribution, and
(b) continuous variation in the
height of adult male humans,
showing a normal distribution about
the mean*

continuous distribution of values. If we were to measure all the adult males in an area, group them into classes that differed from each other by 2 cm and plot a distribution curve, we would obtain a normal distribution. We would probably find that most values would be around 170 cm, the mean value. An individual can be measured and classified using features that vary continuously.

In the early years of genetics, it was difficult to determine to what extent such characters as height or mass, which show this type of continuous variation, are controlled by genes or are the effects of environmental factors. A Danish geneticist, Johannsen, working in the early 1900s, designed a series of experiments to find out if seed mass in the dwarf bean *Phaseolus vulgaris* was inherited or varied due to environmental factors (Figure 6.3). He collected a number of 'pure lines' of seeds, each one consisting of the descendants of one seed. The seeds in each line were genetically identical and each line had a different mean seed mass. In one experiment, he mixed seeds from all these lines together and then selected a sample of large seeds and a sample of small seeds. He grew these and collected the seeds from the offspring of each sample and determined the mean seed mass. He found that the mean seed mass produced from the offspring of the larger seeds was greater than the mean seed mass from the offspring of the smaller seeds. He compared these results with another experiment in which he selected a sample of large seeds and a sample of small seeds from the same pure line. When these were grown and the seeds from the offspring collected, both samples had the same mean seed mass.

(a)

(b)

*Figure 6.2 Adult fruit flies (*Drosophila melanogaster*) with (a) normal (wild-type) and (b) vestigial-winged phenotypes (appearances)*

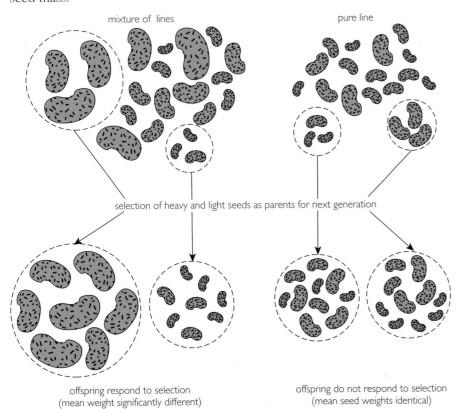

Figure 6.3 Johannsen's experiment with the dwarf bean showed that genes control measurable characteristics and that it is possible to distinguish variation caused by genetic and environmental factors

When Johannsen selected from the mixture of lines, he would have picked out seeds that were genetically different, but when he selected from one line, they were genetically identical and the differences in size were due only to different environmental influences. His experiment showed that measurable variation was controlled by genes and that it was possible to distinguish between hereditary factors and environmental ones. Johannsen did not relate the difference to any particular genes.

Later experiments on grain colour in wheat showed that a number of different genes contribute to characters that show continuous variation and the **multiple gene hypothesis** was put forward. In wheat, the grains vary in colour from white to red and this character is now known to be controlled by two genes, which have a cumulative, or additive, effect.

The term **polygenes** is now used instead of multiple genes and **polygenic inheritance** describes this type of inheritance. Its main features are that:
- the characters are controlled by a number of genes
- individual genes have a small effect
- there is considerable environmental influence
- the characters show a continuous range of variation.

Monohybrid inheritance

Before we consider how characters are inherited, it is worthwhile becoming familiar with some of the terms used in the study of inheritance. From Chapter 5, we already have a definition for a gene as a specific length of DNA coding for a polypeptide. It occupies a specific site on a chromosome, called a **locus**.

An allele is an alternative form of a gene occupying the same locus on a chromosome as other alternative alleles of the same gene. There are at least two forms of each gene. For example, in Mendel's experiments on peas, he investigated two alleles of the gene for stem length: tall and dwarf. When homologous chromosomes pair up during prophase I of meiosis, these alleles would occupy corresponding positions opposite each other (Figure 6.4).

The alleles are responsible for determining contrasting traits of a character, in this case the character is stem length and the traits are tall (represented by **T**) and dwarf (represented by **t**).

The term **genotype** is used to describe the genetic constitution of an organism for the character under consideration. It is represented by the alleles present, so a tall plant would have the genotype **TT** or **Tt**, and a dwarf plant **tt**.

The **phenotype** is the appearance of the character in an organism. It results from an interaction between the expression of the genotype and the effect of the environment. Mendel's pea plants appeared tall or dwarf.

In a diploid organism, since the alleles occur in pairs, one on each homologous chromosome, there is usually a **dominant** allele, which influences the appearance of the phenotype even if it is present with the alternative allele. It

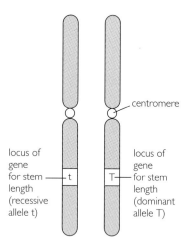

Figure 6.4 A pair of homologous chromosomes, showing that different versions (alleles) of a gene occupy the same position (locus) on a chromosome

centromere

locus of gene for stem length (recessive allele t)

locus of gene for stem length (dominant allele T)

is the convention to represent this dominant allele with a capital letter. The **recessive** allele can only influence the appearance of the phenotype if it is present with an identical allele in the genotype. The recessive allele is represented by a lower case (small) letter. In the case of the peas, tall is dominant to dwarf, so plants with the genotype **TT** or **Tt** will appear tall but **tt** will be dwarf.

If both alleles at a given locus are the same, the organism is said to be **homozygous** for that particular character. **TT** indicates that a pea plant is homozygous for tallness, and **tt** that it is homozygous for dwarfness. If the alleles at a given locus are different, then the organism is said to be **heterozygous** for that particular character. A plant with the genotype **Tt** will be heterozygous for tallness.

Monohybrid cross

A monohybrid cross involves a single character that is controlled by one gene with two or more alleles. Mendel, whose experiments on the inheritance of characters in the garden pea (*Pisum sativum*) led to the formulation of two fundamental laws of genetics, carried out a large number of monohybrid crosses. He had identified a number of distinct varieties of the garden pea, each showing contrasting traits of a particular character, such as tall or dwarf stem length, axially or terminally positioned flowers and purple or white flower colour. He selected pure-breeding plants with the contrasting traits and cross-fertilised them, producing **hybrids**.

If we take flower colour as an example, Mendel had to be sure that the parental types, one with purple flowers and one with white flowers, were pure-breeding. That is to say, when allowed to self-pollinate, they will only produce offspring with one type of flower colour, generation after generation. He then removed the stamens from plants with purple flowers and dusted pollen from white flowers on to their stigmas. He also carried out the reciprocal cross, in which pollen from plants with purple flowers was dusted on to the stigmas of white flowers from which the stamens had been removed (Figure 6.5).

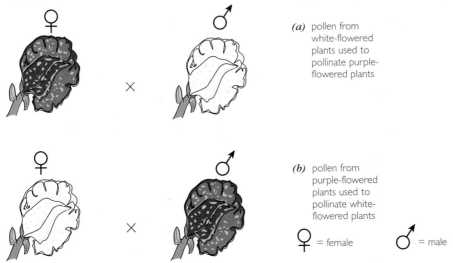

(a) pollen from white-flowered plants used to pollinate purple-flowered plants

(b) pollen from purple-flowered plants used to pollinate white-flowered plants

♀ = female   ♂ = male

Figure 6.5 Mendel carried out reciprocal crosses in his breeding experiments with peas in order to show that the sex of the plant did not affect the outcome of the experiment

Parents: AA   ×   aa
purple-flowered   white-flowered
parents   parents

Gametes: A   a

First filial (F$_1$):   Aa
purple flowers

F$_1$ self-pollinated:
Aa   ×   Aa
Gametes: A   a   A   a

Punnett square for F$_1$ × F$_1$:	F$_1$ gametes	
	A	a
F$_1$ gametes A	AA purple	Aa purple
a	Aa purple	aa white

Second filial (F$_2$):
Genotypes:	AA	Aa	aa
Phenotypes:	purple flowers	purple flowers	white flowers
Ratio:	1	2	: 1

3

Figure 6.7 Convention for describing a genetic cross, showing that the possible combinations between gametes can be expressed in a Punnett square. The events of meiosis explain how the alleles (A and a) are separated to form the gametes

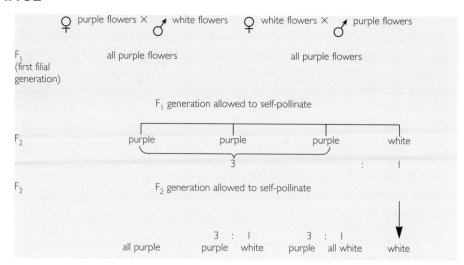

Figure 6.6 In a monohybrid cross with pure-breeding parent plants, when two of their offspring (F$_1$ generation) are allowed to self-fertilise, the ratio of phenotypes in the F$_2$ generation is 3:1. Further self-pollination of the F$_2$ plants to produce the F$_3$ generation will indicate which of the F$_2$ plants were pure-breeding

The seeds of all the plants were collected and planted the following year. When these plants, known as the **first filial (or F$_1$) generation**, flowered, all the flowers were purple. This suggested to Mendel that purple flower colour was dominant to white. He allowed the flowers in the F$_1$ generation to self-pollinate, collected the seeds and planted them the following year. In this, the **second filial generation** (or F$_2$) there were both purple-flowered plants and white-flowered plants, but the ones with purple flowers were three times as frequent as those with white flowers, a ratio of 3:1. Mendel went on to analyse the offspring of this F$_2$ generation by allowing these flowers to self-pollinate (Figure 6.6). He found that the white-flowered plants of the F$_2$ only gave rise to white-flowered plants in the F$_3$ (**the third filial generation**), but one third of the purple-flowered plants produced offspring with purple flowers and two thirds produced a mixture of plants with purple flowers and plants with white flowers. The ratio of purple-flowered plants to white-flowered plants was, again, 3:1.

Mendel investigated a number of different characters with one pair of contrasting traits and always found very similar results and ratios. From such experiments, he worked out his **principle of segregation**, in which he suggested that the characteristics of an organism are determined by factors that occur in pairs, and only one of a pair of factors can be represented in a single gamete. He thought of the units of inheritance as 'particles' and that they were passed from generation to generation. He recognised that sometimes their effects were hidden, but that the particles themselves were passed on unchanged (see Practical: Investigating monohybrid segregation in tobacco).

We can explain what is happening in the monohybrid cross in terms of modern genetics (Figure 6.7). Because the parent plants are homozygous for flower colour, they each produce only one type of gamete. Fertilisation results in a heterozygous hybrid F$_1$ containing one dominant allele and one recessive allele, so the phenotype is purple. As the F$_1$ plants are all heterozygous, when

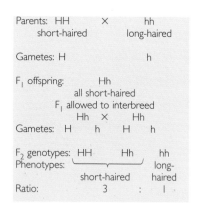

Parents: HH   ×   hh
short-haired   long-haired

Gametes: H   h

F$_1$ offspring: Hh
all short-haired
F$_1$ allowed to interbreed
Hh   ×   Hh
Gametes: H   h   H   h

F$_2$ genotypes: HH   Hh   hh
Phenotypes: long-
      short-haired   haired
Ratio: 3   :   1

Figure 6.8 Results of a monohybrid cross between a homozygous (H H) short-haired guinea pig and a homozygous (hh) long-haired guinea pig, followed by interbreeding of the F$_1$ offspring

gametes are formed, half of them will carry the dominant allele and half the recessive. Fertilisation is random, so the possibilities are that about $\frac{1}{4}$ of the offspring will be homozygous dominant (AA), $\frac{1}{4}$ will be homozygous recessive (**aa**) and $\frac{1}{2}$ will be heterozygous (**Aa**), giving a genotypic ratio of 1:2:1. As **A** is dominant to **a**, then the phenotypic ratio will be 3 purple:1 white.

The events of meiosis explain how the alleles are separated. The inheritance of certain characters in animals follows the same pattern of inheritance as Mendel discovered in the pea plants (see Practical: A breeding experiment using *Tribolium*). In guinea pigs, short hair (**H**) is dominant to long hair (**h**). A pure-breeding short-haired guinea pig (**HH**) was mated with a pure-breeding long-haired guinea pig (**hh**). All the offspring in the F$_1$ had short hair. A male and a female from this generation were allowed to interbreed (Figure 6.8). They produced offspring (the F$_2$), some with short hair and some with long hair, in the ratio of 3 short hair: 1 long hair.

In this example, the offspring that have short hair are either homozygous, **HH,** or heterozygous, **Hh**. The genotype of the long-haired offspring must be **hh**, the homozygous recessive. In order to discover the genotype of one of the short-haired offspring, it is necessary to carry out a test cross, or back cross (Figure 6.9). This involves mating the guinea pig of unknown genotype with a homozygous recessive, which must be **hh**.

If the unknown genotype is **HH**, then the offspring of the test cross will always have short hair, because they will inherit a dominant allele from that parent. If the unknown genotype is **Hh**, the offspring can either inherit **H** or **h**. If any of the offspring have long hair, then we know that the unknown genotype must be **Hh**. The ratio of the offspring in such a test cross, where one parent is heterozygous and the other is the homozygous recessive, is always 1 heterozygous: 1 homozygous recessive.

Dominance

The characters that Mendel investigated all showed complete dominance, where one allele influences the appearance of the phenotype, even if it is present with an alternative allele. So, the homozygous dominant and the heterozygote both have the same phenotype and cannot be distinguished from one another. There are situations where the heterozygotes appear to be intermediate between the two homozygotes. The intermediate cannot be considered to be due to 'blending' of the two alleles, because they separate out when two heterozygotes are interbred. This is known as incomplete dominance or partial dominance, and can be illustrated by the inheritance of flower colour in snapdragons (*Antirrhinum sp.*), where there are two alleles, red and white. Neither allele is dominant and when red and white-flowered plants are crossed the heterozygote produces pink flowers, intermediate between the two homozygotes (Figure 6.10). Self-pollination of the pink heterozygotes of the F$_1$ results in flowers of all three colours, in the ratio 1 red : 2 pink : 1 white, in the F$_2$.

The genotypic ratio of 1 : 2 : 1 is typical of a monohybrid cross, and in this case the phenotypic ratio is the same because the heterozygote colour is not the same as the two homozygotes.

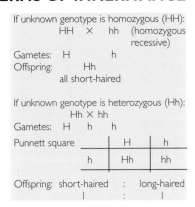

Figure 6.9 shows:

If unknown genotype is homozygous (HH):
HH × hh (homozygous recessive)
Gametes: H h
Offspring: Hh
all short-haired

If unknown genotype is heterozygous (Hh):
Hh × hh
Gametes: H h h
Punnett square

	H	h
h	Hh	hh

Offspring: short-haired : long-haired
1 : 1

*Figure 6.9 Results of the test crosses with long-haired (*hh*) guinea pigs, used to distinguish between short-haired homozygous (*H H*) and short-haired heterozygous (*H h*) individuals*

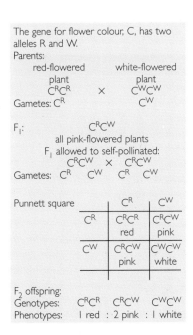

The gene for flower colour, C, has two alleles R and W.
Parents:
red-flowered plant — white-flowered plant
C^{R}C^R × C^{W}C^W
Gametes: C^R — C^W

F$_1$:
C^{R}C^W
all pink-flowered plants
F$_1$ allowed to self-pollinated:
C^{R}C^W × C^{R}C^W
Gametes: C^R C^W — C^R C^W

Punnett square

	C^R	C^W
C^R	C^{R}C^R red	C^{R}C^W pink
C^W	C^{R}C^W pink	C^{W}C^W white

F$_2$ offspring:
Genotypes: C^{R}C^R C^{R}C^W C^{W}C^W
Phenotypes: 1 red : 2 pink : 1 white

Figure 6.10 Incomplete, or partial, dominance in snapdragons (Antirrhinum sp.), showing how it leads to the appearance of a new phenotype in the heterozygous condition

Figure 6.11 Scanning electronmicrograph of red blood cells from an individual suffering from sickle-cell anaemia, showing that some of the cells are misshapen as a result of a mutant allele for one of the polypeptide chains in haemoglobin

Table 6.1 *ABO blood system genotypes and phenotypes*

Genotype	Phenotype
$I^A I^A$	A
$I^A I^O$	A
$I^B I^B$	B
$I^B I^O$	B
$I^A I^B$	AB
$I^O I^O$	O

Parents:
Phenotypes: group A   group B
Genotypes: $I^A I^O$ $I^B I^O$
Gametes: I^A I^O I^B I^O

Punnett square		I^A	I^O
	I^B	$I^A I^B$ Group AB	$I^B I^O$ Group B
	I^O	$I^A I^O$ Group A	$I^O I^O$ Group O

Figure 6.12 Genetic cross between a blood group A individual and a blood group B individual, illustrating that all four blood group phenotypes are equally possible in their offspring

Another situation where the 1:2:1 ratio occurs in the F_2 is seen in codominance, in which both alleles are expressed in the phenotype and the heterozygote has the characters of both parents. There are codominant alleles in both the ABO and MN blood group systems, which will be discussed later in this chapter. Codominance is also shown in the inheritance of the mutant allele that codes for the production of an abnormal β-globin chain in haemoglobin. This allele (Hb^S) codes for the amino acid valine instead of glutamic acid on the β-globin chain and results in the formation of haemoglobin S, responsible for the condition known as sickle-cell anaemia. If an individual is homozygous for this allele (Hb^S/Hb^S), the solubility of the haemoglobin is low and it crystallises, causing the red blood cells to be distorted into a crescent or sickle shape (Figure 6.11). Many red blood cells are destroyed and the individual suffers from sickle-cell anaemia, a condition that may prove fatal. In heterozygous individuals, Hb^S/Hb^A, where Hb^A is the allele for normal haemoglobin, half the haemoglobin is affected and half is normal. In these individuals, the red blood cells are not usually affected, but if their blood is kept in conditions of low oxygen concentration, and the red cells observed, some will be seen to be sickle-shaped. In this case, both alleles contribute to the phenotype and the heterozygotes can be identified by looking at the red blood cells.

Multiple alleles

When there are three or more alleles for a specific locus, a gene is said to have multiple alleles. In any diploid organism, a gene can only be represented twice, that is, one allele on corresponding loci of the homologous chromosome pair concerned. Where there are multiple alleles, the number of phenotypes will depend on the number of alleles and what sort of dominance is shown.

In humans, the ABO blood group system involves three different alleles. The gene locus is represented by I (for isohaemagglutinogen) and determines which form of antigen is secreted on to the surface of the red blood cells. The three alleles are I^A, I^B and I^O. I^A and I^B are codominant and code for slightly different antigens, but I^O is recessive to both I^A and I^B and produces no antigens. An individual carries two alleles, so there are six possible genotypes and four possible phenotypes (Table 6.1).

From the table, it can be seen that individuals with blood group A can either be homozygous for I^A ($I^A I^A$) or heterozygous ($I^A I^O$). Similarly, individuals with blood group B can either be $I^B I^B$ or $I^B I^O$. Individuals with blood group AB are heterozygotes ($I^A I^B$), whilst those with group O must be homozygous recessive ($I^O I^O$). An understanding of this system enables the blood groups within families to be worked out and is of practical importance in relation to blood transfusions (Figure 6.12).

Another example of a multiple allele system is seen in the gene for the determination of coat colour in rabbits, where there are four alleles:
- agouti (C) is the colour of the fur of the wild rabbit and each hair has a grey base, a yellow band and a black tip
- chinchilla (c^{ch}) with silvery, grey coloured fur, the hairs lack the yellow band

- himalayan (**c^h**) has a white coat except for black nose, ears, feet and tail
- albino (**c**) with no pigment, the fur is pure white.

Development of the pigment in the fur of the extremities of the himalayan rabbit is due to a temperature-sensitive enzyme, that only exerts its effect below a certain temperature. Baby himalayans are pure white and only develop their dark colouring when they leave the nest. This is an example of an interaction between the genotype and the environment resulting in the production of a phenotype.

The dominance sequence is $C > c^{ch} > c^h > c$. There are ten possible genotypes but only four possible phenotypes (Table 6.2).

Pedigree analysis in humans

There are a number of distinctive characters in humans that are due to alleles of a single gene and show monohybrid inheritance. It is not possible to carry out experimental crosses in the same way as we can with pea plants and guinea pigs, but information about the pattern of inheritance can be gained from medical records and through the pedigrees of the families concerned. A pedigree is a diagram of a family tree over a number of generations and it shows how the ancestors and descendants are related. This information is of especial importance if it concerns the inheritance of a serious condition, such as thalassaemia (a severe form of anaemia), cystic fibrosis or Huntington's chorea. Analysis of the family pedigree may indicate the likelihood of the condition occurring and in some cases enable prospective parents to check whether or not they possess a faulty gene, before they decide to have children.

In a pedigree diagram, females are shown as circles and males as squares. A solid, filled-in symbol indicates that an individual is affected. For example, albinism is caused by a recessive allele. Affected individuals lack an enzyme necessary for the formation of the pigment melanin, so they have white hair, pale skin, pink eyes and poor eyesight (Figure 6.13).

Table 6.2 *Table of phenotypes and genotypes of rabbits*

Phenotype	Genotype
agouti	CC, Cc^ch, Cc^h, Cc
chinchilla	c^ch c^ch, c^ch c^h, c^ch c
himalayan	c^h c^h, c^h c
albino	cc

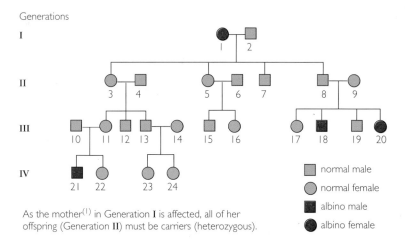

As the mother[1] in Generation **I** is affected, all of her offspring (Generation **II**) must be carriers (heterozygous).

Figure 6.13 Pedigree diagram, or family tree, showing the inheritance of albinism through four generations. Such diagrams are valuable in predicting the genotypes of particular individuals

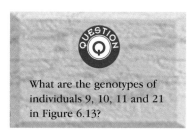

What are the genotypes of individuals 9, 10, 11 and 21 in Figure 6.13?

Dihybrid inheritance

Following his experiments on monohybrid inheritance, Mendel carried out a second set of experiments to investigate the inheritance of two pairs of contrasting characters. He made dihybrid crosses between pure-breeding pea plants differing in two characters. From his monohybrid crosses, he knew that the trait for round seeds (**R**) was dominant to that for wrinkled seeds (**r**) and that the trait for yellow cotyledons (**Y**) was dominant to that for green cotyledons (**y**). So he crossed plants with round seeds and yellow cotyledons (**RRYY**) with plants that had wrinkled seeds and green cotyledons (**rryy**). The F_1 generation all had the dominant characters of round seeds and yellow cotyledons. When these were self-pollinated, the F_2 generation had four different phenotypes: two that resembled the parental types and two new types, combining characters of both parents (Figure 6.14). The phenotypes and the ratios of plants obtained in the F_2 were as follows:

- 9 (round seeds and yellow cotyledons)
- 3 (round seeds and green cotyledons)
- 3 (wrinkled seeds and yellow cotyledons)
- 1 (wrinkled seeds and green cotyledons)

Mendel observed that the ratio of round seeds to wrinkled seeds was 3:1 and that the ratio for yellow and green cotyledons was also 3:1, the same ratios as appeared in the monohybrid crosses. He saw that the two 3:1 ratios were associated in the same cross and deduced that the two pairs of characters behave quite independently of one another. This led him to formulate his principle of independent assortment, in which he stated that any one of a pair of characteristics may combine with any one of another pair.

Parents:		RRYY round seeds yellow cotyledons	×		rryy wrinkled seeds green cotyledons
Gametes:		RY			ry
F_1			RrYy round seeds yellow cotyledons		
F_1 allowed to self-pollinate	RrYy		×		RrYy

Gametes		RY	Ry	rY	ry
	RY	RRYY round, yellow	RRYy round, yellow	RrYY round, yellow	RrYy round, yellow
	Ry	RRYy round, yellow	RRyy round, green	RrYy round, yellow	Rryy round, green
	rY	RrYY round, yellow	RrYy round, yellow	rrYY wrinkled, yellow	rrYy wrinkled, yellow
	ry	RrYy round, yellow	Rryy round, green	rrYy wrinkled, yellow	rryy wrinkled, green

F_2 9 round, yellow   :   3 round, green   :   3 wrinkled, yellow   :   1 wrinkled, green

round to wrinkled
3 : 1

yellow to green
3 : 1

Figure 6.14 Dihybrid inheritance of independent characters, illustrated by Mendel's cross between pea plants with round seeds and yellow cotyledons and plants with wrinkled seeds and green cotyledons. Following self-pollination of the F_1 plants, the ratio of phenotypes in the F_2 generation is 9:3:3:1

We can explain the results of Mendel's experiments in terms of what we know about alleles and the behaviour of chromosomes during meiosis. The pure-breeding plants, being diploid, will possess two alleles for each character. During gamete formation, meiosis occurs and the gametes will contain one allele for each character. In the F_1 generation, the genotype can only be **RrYy**, and when these plants are self-pollinated, there are four possible combinations in both the male and female gametes: **RY**, **Ry**, **rY** and **ry**. Because fertilisation is random, and any male gamete can fuse with any female gamete, there are 16 possible combinations, as shown in the Punnett square. We know there are four different phenotypes, but these are produced by nine different genotypes. These outcomes are summarised in Table 6.3.

Table 6.3 *Phenotypes and genotypes in dihybrid inheritance*

Phenotype	Genotypes
round seeds, yellow cotyledons	RRYY RRYy RrYY RrYy
round seeds, green cotyledons	RRyy Rryy
wrinkled seeds, yellow cotyledons	rrYY rrYy
wrinkled seeds, green cotyledons	rryy

In order to verify that there were nine different genotypes and that there were four possible combinations in the gametes, Mendel carried out further crosses. He grew the plants from the seeds of the F_2, allowed them to self-pollinate and collected all the progeny from this F_3 generation. He found that the F_2 that had wrinkled seeds and green cotyledons only gave rise to plants that produced wrinkled seeds and green cotyledons. With the plants that produced wrinkled seeds and yellow cotyledons in the F_2, he found one third of them bred true, producing offspring with wrinkled seeds and yellow cotyledons, but two thirds of them did not. They were pure-breeding for wrinkled seeds, but the cotyledon character appeared in the ratio 3 yellow : 1 green. He obtained similar results for those plants that had round seeds and green cotyledons, but in this case all the plants bred true for the cotyledon character and it was the seed form that varied. Mendel also carried out a test cross using the F_1 genotype and the pure-breeding parental type with wrinkled seeds and green cotyledons. The results of this cross are illustrated in Figure 6.15. The results of this test cross provided evidence that four types of gametes were produced and that they were present in equal proportions.

As we have seen, in this dihybrid cross, two of the phenotypes in the F_2 were like the original parents and two showed new combinations of characters. This process by which new combinations of characters arise is known as **recombination** and the individuals that have the new combination of characters are called recombinants. Recombination is important as it can lead to genetic variation and accounts for many of the small differences between individuals in a natural population.

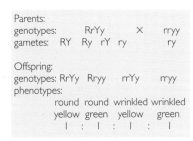

Figure 6.15 Test cross in dihybrd inheritance, showing that four types of gametes are produced in equal proportions by the F_1 (heterozygous, RrYy) plants

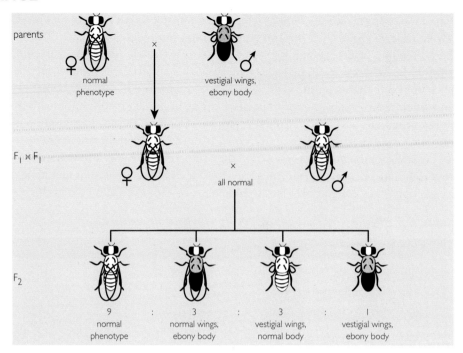

Figure 6.16 Dihybrid cross in Drosophila, *illustrating inheritance of wing form and body colour, and showing that the alleles for vestigial wings and ebony body are recessive*

Dihybrid inheritance can be demonstrated in other organisms, and the cross illustrated in Figure 6.16 shows the inheritance of body colour and wing form in the fruit fly, *Drosophila melanogaster* (see Figure 6.2). *Drosophila* has been used extensively in genetics experiments because it is easy to keep under laboratory conditions, it has a short life cycle of ten days and only four pairs of chromosomes.

Linkage

In the early 1900s, after the rediscovery of Mendel's work, many experimental dihybrid crosses were carried out in an attempt to verify Mendel's ratios, but not all of these gave the 9:3:3:1 ratio. One such cross was carried out by Bateson and Punnett using sweet peas with different flower colour and pollen characteristics. They crossed sweet peas having purple flowers and long pollen with plants having red flowers and round pollen. The F_1 produced plants having purple flowers and long pollen, so Bateson and Punnett knew which were the dominant traits. The F_1 were allowed to self-pollinate and in the F_2 most of the offspring resembled the original parents with a small number of recombinants. The results are shown in Table 6.4. Alongside Bateson and Punnett's figures are the numbers expected if the F_2 ratio was 9:3:3:1.

Table 6.4 *Results of Bateson and Punnett's experiment*

Phenotype	Results	Expected results
purple flower, long pollen	296	240
purple flower, round pollen	19	80
red flower, long pollen	27	80
red flower, round pollen	85	27

If we just look at flower colour, we can work out that there were 315 purple-flowered plants and 112 red-flowered plants, which is approximately a 3:1 ratio. Looking at the results overall, the ratio of the original parental types is much closer to a 3:1 ratio than it is to a 9:3:3:1. The results of this experiment, together with other evidence, led geneticists to suggest that some characters tend to be inherited together. In the light of our knowledge of the structure of chromosomes, it now seems obvious that there are large numbers of genes on each chromosome and that these genes will usually be inherited together. What seems surprising is that Mendel selected characters that are on separate chromosomes, especially as the haploid number of chromosomes in the garden pea is 7. Was he lucky, or did he select his characters carefully?

Genes located on the same chromosome are said to be linked and a linkage group consists of all the genes on a single chromosome. In Bateson and Punnett's experiment, the genes for flower colour and pollen shape are on the same chromosome and inherited together. This accounts for the large numbers of the original parental types in the F_2, but we can see that the linkage is not complete as there are small numbers of recombinants. These can be accounted for by the crossing over that can occur during prophase I of meiosis (Figure 6.17).

Complete linkage, where there is no crossing over during meiosis and consequently no recombinants among the offspring, is rare, but it does occur

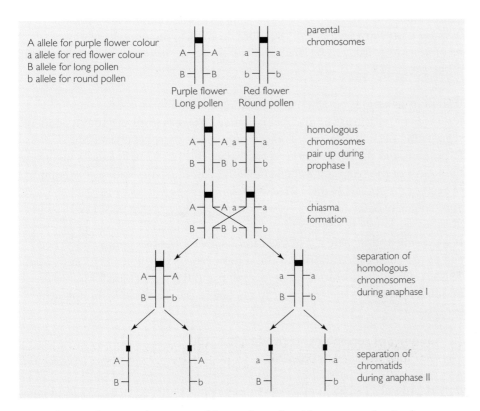

Figure 6.17 Explanation of Bateson and Punnett's results with sweet pea, showing how crossing over between chromatids during prophase I of meiosis can produce a small proportion of recombinants

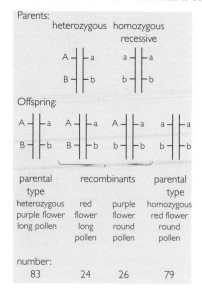

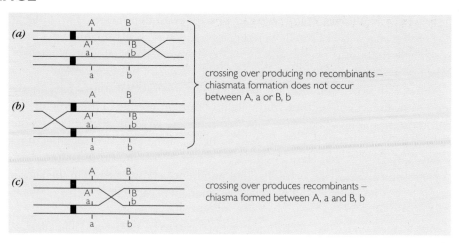

Figure 6.18 Diagrams illustrating that the site of chiasma formation and subsequent crossing over between chromatids determines whether or not recombinants occur

Figure 6.19 Results of test cross with sweet pea, confirming that the genes for flower colour and pollen shape are linked in sweet pea and that recombination has occurred to separate the alleles in the linkage group

in some flowering plants, such as *Fritillaria*, and a few insects. Genes located on the same chromosome more often show partial linkage, because there is usually at least one chiasma formed somewhere within a bivalent. Crossing over produces two kinds of recombinants in approximately equal numbers, because of the way in which the non-sister chromatids break and rejoin, but it will not always occur between the two genes concerned. Figure 6.18 shows what can happen: in *(a)* and *(b)* there is no crossing-over between the two genes, but in *(c)* there is. As this will occur in some cells and not others, and because it only involves two of the four chromatids, the number of recombinants is likely to be small and will always occur in less than 50 per cent of the progeny.

If an unusual ratio is obtained in a breeding experiment, it is necessary to do a test cross or back cross to discover whether linkage is involved. If independent segregation occurs, then the expected ratio in a test cross between the F_1 progeny and the homozygous recessive will be 1:1:1:1. If linkage is involved, then most of the offspring will resemble the parental types with a small number of each of the recombinants. The two parental types will occur in approximately equal numbers, as will the recombinants (Figure 6.19).

It is possible to calculate a crossover frequency for the two genes concerned and to use such data to work out the order of the genes along a chromosome. This is referred to as chromosome mapping and has been done for a number of different species. The crossover frequency is calculated using the following expression:

$$\frac{\textbf{number of recombinants produced} \times \textbf{100}}{\textbf{total number of offspring}}$$

If there are only a small number of recombinants, then the crossover frequency will be small, indicating that the loci of the two genes concerned are situated quite close together and the chances of them being separated during crossing over is quite small.

Interactions between unlinked genes

In the examples of dihybrid crosses discussed so far in this chapter, each of the genes controls a different character, but there are many instances where a single character is influenced by two or more unlinked genes.

Bateson and Punnett worked out the interactions between two unlinked genes that are involved in the determination of comb shape in domestic poultry. There are a number of different forms of the comb and Bateson and Punnett crossed birds with 'pea' combs and birds with 'rose' combs. They knew that both of these types bred true, but the F_1 produced a completely different type of comb shape, called 'walnut'. Interbreeding of these walnut types yielded pea, rose and walnut combs, together with yet another type known as 'single'. The four phenotypes occurred in the ratio 9:3:3:1.

Bateson and Punnett suggested that there were two genes involved, one in which the dominant allele **P** gave rise to the pea form and the other in which the dominant allele **R** gave rise to the rose form. So, the genotypes of the parents in their original cross must have been **PPrr** (pea comb) and **ppRR** (rose comb). The genotype of the F_1 was therefore **PpRr**, interacting to give the walnut comb. In the F_2, the genotype with no dominant alleles, **pprr**, has a single comb (Figure 6.21).

The ratios obtained in this cross are the same as Mendel obtained in his dihybrid crosses and indicate that the two genes are inherited independently. The walnut and single combs are completely new forms of the character, and are due to the interactions between the genes concerned and cannot be thought of as recombinants.

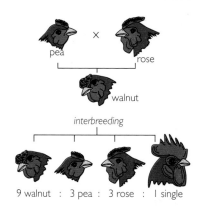

Figure 6.20 Variation in comb shape in poultry due to the interaction between unlinked genes affecting the same characteristic

Parents:	pea comb PPrr		×	rose comb ppRR		
Gametes:	Pr			pR		
F_1 × F_1	walnut PpRr		×	walnut PpRr		
Gametes	PR Pr pR pr			PR Pr pR pr		

male gametes

		PR	Pr	pR	pr
female gametes	PR	PPRR walnut	PPRr walnut	PpRR walnut	PpRr walnut
	Pr	PPRr walnut	PPrr pea	PpRr walnut	Pprr pea
	pR	PpRR walnut	PpRr walnut	ppRR rose	ppRr rose
	pr	PpRr walnut	Pprr pea	ppRr rose	pprr single

9 walnut : 3 pea : 3 rose : 1 single

Figure 6.21 Genetic cross to show how all four comb phenotypes can occur in the F_2 offspring, following interbreeding of the heterozygous, walnut comb F_1 generation

Parents:	white flowers		white flowers
	CCpp	×	ccPP
Gametes:	Cp		cP

$F_1 \times F_1$	purple			purple
	CcPp		×	CcPp
Gametes	CP Cp cP cp			CP Cp cP cp

male gametes

		CP	Cp	cP	cp
F₂ (female gametes)	CP	CCPP purple	CCPp purple	CcPP purple	CcPp purple
	Cp	CCPp purple	CCpp white	CcPp purple	Ccpp white
	cP	CcPP purple	CcPp purple	ccPP white	ccPp white
	cp	CcPp purple	Ccpp white	ccPp white	ccpp white

9 purple : 7 white

Figure 6.22 Genetic cross to illustrate complementary interaction between two genes affecting expression of flower colour in sweet peas, showing that if one of the genes is homozygous recessive the purple colour is not expressed

There are other examples of gene interaction where the ratios are different, but still seem to be multiples of $\frac{1}{16}$. In another investigation carried out by Bateson and Punnett, two pure breeding white-flowered sweet pea plants produced offspring with purple flowers. These purple-flowered plants were self-pollinated and the resulting progeny consisted of plants with purple flowers, and plants with white flowers in the ratio 9 purple : 7 white. In this case, it was suggested that one of the genes (**C**) controls a colourless precursor of the pigment and the other gene (**P**) controls the conversion of this precursor to its purple form. In order for the purple colour to develop, the dominant allele of both genes must be present. The two white-flowered plants must be homozygous dominant for one of the genes in order for purple colour to show up in the offspring. The cross is illustrated in Figure 6.22.

These two genes controlling flower colour are said to be complementary, as they interact together to produce a character which is different from that given by either of them on their own.

Another example of this type of interaction is shown in the inheritance of coat colour in mice. Wild mice have a coat colour referred to as 'agouti', where the individual hairs are black with a yellow band. Agouti (**A**) is dominant to black coat colour (**a**), which is produced by black hairs. The difference is due to a single gene with two alleles. In order for the coat colour pigment to be synthesised, at least one dominant allele of another, independently inherited, gene (**C**) is required. When individuals are homozygous recessive (**cc**) for this second gene, no pigment can be formed and the mice are albino. Figure 6.23 illustrates a cross between a pure-breeding black mouse (**aaCC**) and an albino (**AAcc**), which produces agouti mice (**AaCc**), in the F₁. When F₁ individuals are

Parents:	black aaCC	×	white AAcc

Gametes: aC   Ac

$F_1 \times F_1$ agouti AaCc   ×   agouti AaCc

Gametes   AC Ac aC ac   AC Ac aC ac

F_2

	male gametes			
female gametes	AC	Ac	aC	ac
AC	AACC	AACc	AaCC	AaCc
Ac	AACc	AAcc	AaCc	Aacc
aC	AaCC	AaCc	aaCC	aaCc
ac	AaCc	Aacc	aaCc	aacc

9 agouti : 3 black : 4 albino

Figure 6.23 Inheritance of coat colour in mice by complementary interaction of genes, showing how the gene for hair pigment (C) masks the effect of the gene for coat colour (A) when it is homozygous recessive (cc)

interbred, the resulting offspring include agouti, black and albino mice in the ratio 9 agouti : 3 black : 4 albino.

Both the inheritance of flower colour in the sweet peas and coat colour in mice are examples of **epistasis**, where one gene hides the expression of another gene. In the sweet peas, where a dominant allele of both genes is required to produce flower colour, the homozygous recessive condition of either gene is epistatic to the expression of the other gene. In the mice, the gene for pigment development (**C**) is epistatic to the gene for coat colour when it is homozygous recessive (**cc**).

Sex determination and sex linkage

Sex is genetically determined and matings between males and females of a species always result in two sexes among the offspring. The two sexes occur in approximately equal numbers, the same ratio as would be expected in a monohybrid test cross. Examination of the chromosomes of many mammals and insects indicates that sex determination is associated with the inheritance of a pair of particular chromosomes designated the sex chromosomes, or heterosomes. There are two kinds of sex chromosomes, called the X and the Y. The rest of the chromosomes, apart from the X and the Y, are known as the autosomal chromosomes, or autosomes. The X chromosome is usually larger than the Y, but they pair because they have regions that are homologous. In the non-homologous, or non-pairing, region of the X chromosome there are genes that are not present on the Y chromosome. In many species, the Y chromosome carries very few genes and is often referred to as 'genetically empty'. It is important to realise that, although the sex chromosomes

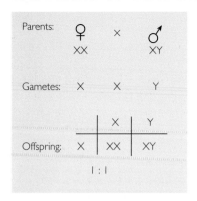

Figure 6.24 Sex determination by the X and Y chromosomes, showing how the 1:1 male:female ratio is achieved and how the male genotype determines the sex of the offspring

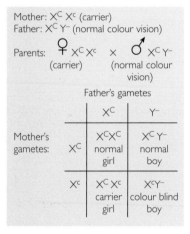

Figure 6.25 Genetic cross between a female carrier of the allelele for colour blindness and a male with normal colour vision, showing how a sex-linked characteristic can be expressed in the offspring

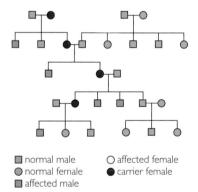

■ normal male ○ affected female
● normal female ● carrier female
■ affected male

Figure 6.26 Pedigree diagram showing the inheritance of red-green colour blindness through five generations

determine the sex of an individual, they do not carry all the genes responsible for the development of the sexual characteristics.

In humans and in insects, the female is referred to as the homogametic sex, as she possesses two X chromosomes (XX) and the male is the heterogametic sex, having one X chromosome and one Y chromosome (XY). The sex chromosomes pair during prophase I of meiosis. They are separated at anaphase I and chromatid separation occurs at anaphase II. Females can only produce eggs that contain a single X chromosome, but males produce sperm with either an X chromosome or a Y chromosome. Due to the events of meiosis, 50 per cent of the sperm carry an X and 50 per cent carry a Y. At fertilisation, there is an equal probability of an egg fusing with a sperm carrying an X as with a sperm carrying a Y. The sex of the offspring is thus determined by the male (Figure 6.24).

In the early stages of development of the human embryo, there are no external signs to indicate its sex, since the reproductive organs are still capable of developing into ovaries or testes. The presence of the Y chromosome triggers the development of testes, probably through the production of higher levels of male hormones. Absence of the Y chromosome results in the formation of ovaries.

In addition to carrying genes that are concerned with the determination of sex, the sex chromosomes carry genes for other characters. It was discovered, when carrying out reciprocal crosses involving the inheritance of eye colour in *Drosophila*, that the outcome depended on which way round the cross was carried out. The results of a cross between a red-eyed female and a white-eyed male were different from the cross between a white-eyed female and a red-eyed male. Any trait that can be shown by both sexes, but which can be seen to be linked to the inheritance of sex, is described as sex-linked. As we have already mentioned, few genes are present on the Y chromosome, so traits that show this type of inheritance are usually controlled by genes located on the non-pairing region of the X chromosome. It would be more accurate to call them X-linked.

Sex-linked genes are responsible for a number of human conditions, such as red-green colour blindness, haemophilia, Duchenne muscular dystrophy and certain types of baldness, which appear more frequently in males than in females (Figures 6.25). If a female carries a recessive allele for one of these conditions on one of her X chromosomes, it is likely that she has a normal, dominant allele on her other X chromosome. She will be heterozygous and not show the condition, but she will be a carrier. On the other hand, if a male has a recessive allele, he will show the trait, as he has only one X chromosome.

In the inheritance of red-green colour blindness shown in Figure 6.25, the allele for normal colour vision is represented by C and that for colour blindness by **c**. The mother is a carrier and the father has normal vision. The probability of the children inheriting the condition is shown to be zero for girls and 50 per cent for boys. The chances of a girl being a carrier, like the mother, are 50 per cent. Figure 6.26 shows a pedigree for an affected family.

Investigating monohybrid segregation in tobacco

Introduction

The synthesis of chlorophyll in tobacco (*Nicotinia tabacum*) plants is controlled by a single pair of alleles. Seedlings that have the dominant allele (**A**) have green cotyledons due to the presence of chlorophyll. Seedlings that are homozygous recessive (**aa**) have pale yellow or white cotyledons because they are unable to synthesise chlorophyll. These are described as chlorotic seedlings and are unable to photosynthesise. They die soon after germination.

Tobacco seeds can be obtained that have been produced by self-pollinating heterozygous (**Aa**) plants. These seeds are very small and can be germinated successfully in a petri dish containing plain agar. The seeds take about two weeks to germinate at room temperature.

Materials

- Supply of tobacco seeds
- Petri dishes containing 2 per cent plain agar, or several sheets of moistened filter paper

Method

1 Scatter 30 to 40 tobacco seeds evenly over the surface of the agar.
2 Replace the petri dish lid, label, and seal with adhesive tape to prevent drying out.
3 Leave the dishes on a window sill, avoiding direct sunlight.
4 When the seeds have germinated, count the numbers of green and chlorotic seedlings.

Results and discussion

1 What phenotypic ratio, green: chlorotic, would you expect in your seedlings?
2 Calculate the expected numbers of green and chlorotic seedlings.
3 Apply a chi-squared test to determine whether your results differ significantly from the expected results.
4 How could you modify this experiment to investigate whether or not chlorophyll synthesis is light dependent?

PATTERNS OF INHERITANCE

A breeding experiment using Tribolium

Introduction

The flour beetle *Tribolium confusum* is a pest of stored cereal products. Both *T. confusum* and *T. castaneum* are useful organisms for breeding experiments and offer a number of advantages over the more familiar *Drosophila*. For example, sex differences are easily determined at the pupal stage, so separation of virgin females is more straightforward (Figure 6.27). The insects do not climb smooth surfaces and the adults do not fly at room temperature.

The developmental periods vary considerably according to temperature and relative humidity (R.H.). For *T. confusum*, the entire life cycle from egg to egg takes 5 to 6 weeks at 25°C and 70 per cent R.H. Insects can be reared in glass tubes (10 cm × 2.5 cm approx.) one-third filled with either wholemeal flour or wheat meal. To maintain constant conditions, these culture tubes should be kept in a desiccator, or other suitable container, within an incubator at 25 °C. A humidity of 70 per cent R.H. can be maintained using a saturated solution of sodium nitrate, placed in the desiccator. The lid should be removed for 30 seconds each day to air the cultures.

When setting up genetic crosses, it is essential to start with virgin females, because females can continue to lay eggs fertilised by stored sperm for some time after the initial mating. The determination of sex of *Tribolium* is best undertaken at the pupal stage. In *T. confusum*, the elytral (anterior wing) striations in the male do not reach the apex, whereas in the female, some of the striations meet at the apex.

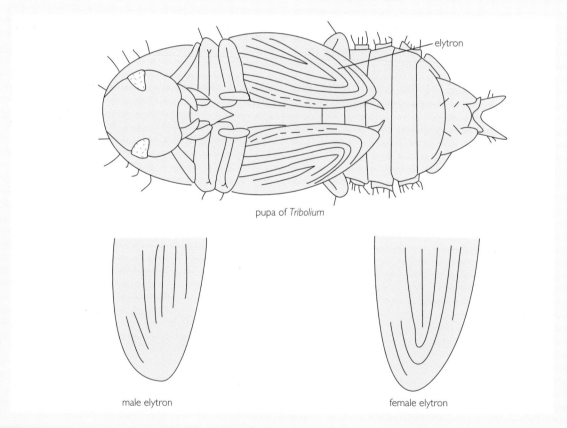

pupa of *Tribolium*

male elytron

female elytron

Figure 6.27 Identification of male and female pupae of Tribolium confusum *according to markings on their elytra*

PATTERNS OF INHERITANCE

Materials

- Stock cultures of *Tribolium confusum*, such as wild type and pearl-eyed
- Desiccator or other suitable container
- Saturated sodium nitrate solution
- Incubator at 25 °C
- Culture tubes, 10 cm × 2.5 cm approx
- Wholemeal flour or wheat meal
- Sieve
- Small paintbrush to manipulate insects
- Binocular microscope or hand lens

TOXIC
sodium
nitrate

Method

1 Sieve the stock cultures, sex and segregate male and female pupae. Incubate until adult. Alternatively, crosses may be made up starting with pupae.
2 Set up crosses, such as one female wild type and two pearl-eyed males, in tubes of food medium.
3 Incubate at 25 °C and 70 per cent R.H.
4 After 40 to 45 days, remove the adults. Then, once or twice a week, remove all emerged F_1 adults and set up crosses for the F_2.
5 Incubate the F_2 crosses and proceed as in step 4. Collect and score the F_2 adults until the whole generation has emerged.

Results and discussion

1 What phenotypic ratio would you expect in your F_2?
2 Calculate the expected numbers of each phenotype in your F_2.
3 Apply a chi-squared test to investigate whether or not your results differ significantly from the expected results.

Further work

1 Set up crosses other than that suggested.
2 Investigate the effect of temperature on the developmental periods of *Tribolium*.

7 Sources of new variation

Meiosis and random variation

The process of meiosis is described in Chapter 5. Meiosis contributes to genetic variation by increasing the potential for genetic variability in gamete formation. This variability can arise by two mechanisms, independent assortment and crossing over leading to recombination. Random fertilisation during sexual reproduction further increases the potential for genetic variation.

Consider a cross between two maize plants, both of which are heterozygous for a gene that controls the colour of the grains. The dominant allele **A** produces purple grains and the recessive allele **a** results in white grains (Figure 7.1). Heterozygous plants will therefore have the genotype **Aa**. Meiosis results in the separation (or segregation) of alleles so that half of the gametes will carry the **A** allele and half the **a** allele. If fertilisation occurs at random, there is an equal probability of fertilisation of an **A** egg and an **a** egg with a male gamete irrespective of whether the male gamete is **A** or **a**. What will be the genotypes of the fertilised eggs?

This question can be easily answered by drawing up a Punnett square to show the possible combinations of male and female gametes (Figure 7.2).

The predicted ratio of genotypes is therefore 1 **AA** : 2 **Aa** : 1 **aa**. How does this model help to explain the ratio of phenotypes in the offspring? Since **a** (the allele for purple grains) is dominant, we would expect a 3 : 1 ratio of purple : white grains. Plants with purple grains will have the genotypes of either **AA** or **Aa**, and white-grained plants will have the genotype **aa**, in other words there is a 3 : 1 ratio of the phenotypes purple : white.

The observed ratio might not, however, be exactly 3 : 1. It is possible, for example, that more **A** male gametes succeed in fertilising the eggs, so the ratio would be rather more than 3 : 1 of purple to white grains. The larger the sample, the closer the observed ratio approaches 3 : 1.

Mutation

During the process of replication, DNA is normally copied exactly so that the genetic material remains the same from generation to generation. However, very occasionally, changes can occur so that an organism may inherit altered genetic material. Such inherited changes are known as **mutations**. Mutation is another source of genetic variability in a population and it can occur spontaneously. The frequency with which one allele mutates to another is known as the mutation rate. For example, the mutation rate for maize purple grains is 1×10^{-5}. This means that out of 10^5 alleles for white grains, only one (that is one in one hundred thousand) mutates to an allele for the purple grain every generation.

Figure 7.1 Sweet corn (maize), showing production of purple and white seeds in a single cob

| | genotypes of male gametes | |
	A	a
A	AA	Aa
a	Aa	aa

genotypes of female gametes

Figure 7.2 Punnett square illustrating possible combinations of A *and* a *gametes from two parents*

Altered DNA molecules faithfully replicate the changed sequences so that the mutant genes are passed on to successive generations. The spontaneous mutation rate is essential for providing new variation necessary for survival in a changing environment, in other words it provides the raw material for evolutionary change.

Mutagens and point mutations

Mutagens are physical or chemical agents that greatly increase the mutation rate. Mutagens include ultraviolet light and X-rays, which damage DNA in various ways, and certain chemical substances, which alter DNA by adding or deleting one or more bases in a sequence. Chemical mutagens include nitrous acid and 5-bromouracil. Nitrous acid acts directly on nucleic acids, and alters the genetic code by converting one base into another. For example, cytosine is converted into uracil, which bonds to adenine instead of guanine.

Such changes in the sequence of bases are referred to as point mutations and include deletion, insertion and substitution mutations. Figure 7.3 illustrates these types of mutation.

What are the consequences of these changes in the base sequence?

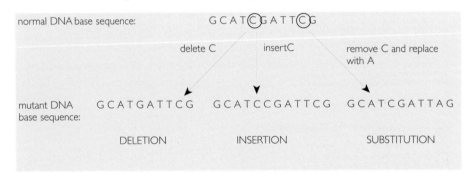

Figure 7.3 Mechanisms by which deletion, insertion and substitution mutations can arise

You will recall that, during protein synthesis, the sequence of bases in DNA is transcribed into a complementary sequence of bases in messenger RNA (mRNA), which is then translated into a sequence of amino acids. Each sequence of three bases is a code for a specific amino acid, so that if the code is altered, this may result in an incorrect sequence of amino acids. Consider the effect of base deletion, for example, on the sequence of amino acids. Codons are separated to make the changes clearer.

Normal DNA sequence:

GAC TTC AGT CTA

complementary mRNA sequence:

CUG AAG UCA GAU

amino acid sequence:

Leu – Lys – Ser – Asp

Now suppose that the first C in the normal DNA sequence is deleted.

Mutant DNA sequence:

GAT TCA GTC TA

complementary mRNA sequence:

CUA AGU CAG AU

amino acid sequence:

Leu – Ser – Glu–

Q

Suggest what would be the likely effect of a deletion mutation followed by an addition mutation in a different part of the same gene.

The effect on the sequence of amino acids from this small change in the DNA bases is profound. Every amino acid after the change might be replaced by a different amino acid. Base deletion has resulted in a shift of the 'reading frame' so that all subsequent codons are altered. Since the order of amino acids is responsible for the final shape and functional properties of the completed protein, it is not surprising that mutation can result in the synthesis of a totally different protein.

We can illustrate the effect of point mutation by reference to a specific example. Sickle-cell anaemia (see Chapter 6) arises because of a substitution mutation in a single codon, which specifies valine instead of glutamic acid in the amino acid sequence of the β-chain in the haemoglobin molecule. This is illustrated in Figure 7.4. The affected codons only are shown.

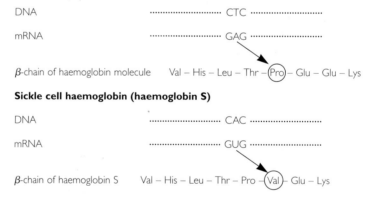

Normal haemoglobin (haemoglobin A)

DNA .... CTC ....

mRNA .... GAG ....

β-chain of haemoglobin molecule   Val – His – Leu – Thr –(Pro)– Glu – Glu – Lys

Sickle cell haemoglobin (haemoglobin S)

DNA .... CAC ....

mRNA .... GUG ....

β-chain of haemoglobin S   Val – His – Leu – Thr – Pro –(Val)– Glu – Lys

Figure 7.4 Effect of substitution mutation on expression of gene for normal haemoglobin (HbA) β-chains, leading to synthesis of sickle-cell haemoglobin (HbS)

This change has a profound effect on the properties of haemoglobin S, which can result in changes in the shape of the red blood cells. Such cells have a shorter life span than normal red blood cells and therefore sufferers are likely to become anaemic. Sickle-cell anaemia is a serious condition, which is often fatal before middle age.

Chromosome mutations

Chromosome mutations can arise in two major ways, either by an alteration in the structure of a chromosome or by an alteration in the number of chromosomes. Changes in structure include **deletion**, where part of a chromosome breaks off and is lost when the cell divides, and **translocation**, where a fragment of one chromosome attaches to another, non-homologous chromosome. One type of translocation, known as reciprocal translocation, involves a two-way exchange of chromosomal segments. This is illustrated in Figure 7.5. The letters are used to indicate regions of each chromosome.

Changes in the number of chromosomes can vary from the duplication or loss of one chromosome (**polysomy**) to duplication of every chromosome, so that there are three or more complete sets of chromosomes (**polyploidy**).

Both changes in the structure and in the numbers of chromosomes have consequences other than their immediate effects on the chromosomes. Individuals who are heterozygous for chromosomes with different structures frequently have reduced fertility, and individuals with altered numbers of chromosomes may be non-viable or sterile.

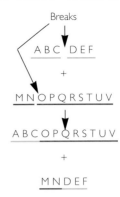

Figure 7.5 Reciprocal translocation of segments between two adjacent chromosomes

Translocation

A translocation is the movement of one part of a chromosome to another, non-homologous chromosome. Translocations can cause several human diseases. For example, about 5 per cent of individuals with Down's syndrome have one parent who is heterozygous for a translocation mutation. This arises because chromosome number 21 attaches to chromosome number 14, forming a translocation heterozygote. A gamete may be produced containing the translocated 14 with the attached 21, plus a normal 21. If this gamete is fertilised, three chromosomes number 21 (trisomy 21) are present in the zygote, which results in Down's syndrome. Fertilisation of the gamete containing no chromosome number 21 results in a zygote with only one 21 chromosome (monosomy 21), which is a lethal genotype. Overall, approximately one-third of the live births arising from this translocation heterozygote will be expected to have Down's syndrome. However, the proportion is less than this, because some Down's individuals do not survive gestation (Figure 7.6).

Polysomy

Polysomy is the general term for the condition in which the number of a particular chromosome is not diploid. Sometimes, during meiosis, a pair of homologous chromosomes will fail to separate properly so that one daughter cell receives an extra chromosome and one daughter cell is left with no chromosome from that pair. This failure of homologous chromosomes to separate is termed **non-disjunction**. When the gametes are fertilised by a normal gamete, the zygote will either have one extra chromosome, that is, $2n+1$, which is termed trisomy, or it will have one missing chromosome, $2n-1$, termed monosomy. Non-disjunction is most common during meiosis I, but it can also occur during meiosis II.

One example of non-disjunction leading to trisomy is Down's syndrome. Although, as described previously, about 5 per cent of cases are a result of a translocation mutation, in about 95 per cent of cases it results from

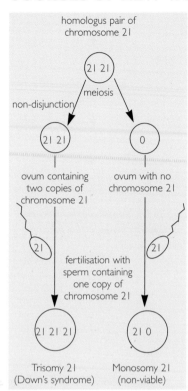

Figure 7.7 *Non-disjunction of chromosome 21 leading to Down's syndrome*

Figure 7.8 *Child with Down's syndrome*

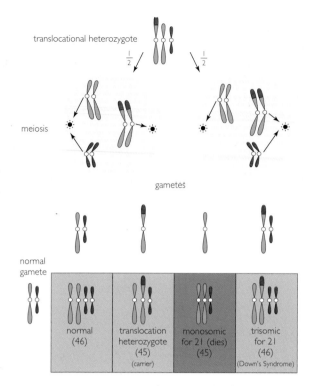

Figure 7.6 Mechanism by which individuals with Down's syndrome result from a translocation mutation (chromosome 14 is shown in blue and chromosome 21 in red)

non-disjunction of chromosome number 21 during meiosis. This is shown in Figure 7.7, where only chromosome number 21 is shown.

Down's syndrome is characterised by mental retardation, distinctive palm prints, and a characteristic facial appearance (Figure 7.8). The incidence of Down's syndrome increases with the age of the mother. For example, the incidence is about 1 in 2300 for mothers aged 20, but rises to about 1 in 40 for mothers aged 45. The exact reason for this is unknown.

Polyploidy

Organisms with three or more complete sets of chromosomes are known as **polyploids**. Polyploidy is relatively common in plants, but rare in animals, occurring only, for example, in certain beetles, earthworms and fish. Many important crop plants are polyploids: potatoes are tetraploid and bread wheat is hexaploid.

There are two major types of polyploids: **autopolyploids**, which receive all their chromosomes from the same species, and **allopolyploids**, which receive their chromosomes from different species. Polyploids can arise naturally when a cell undergoes abnormal meiosis and all the chromosomes go to one pole. This will result in a gamete having the diploid number of chromosomes. In most situations, this diploid gamete would combine with a haploid gamete resulting in a triploid zygote.

To illustrate the development of polyploid plants, the development of hexaploid wheat is shown in Figure 7.9.

Polyploids can be produced artificially using a substance called colchicine, which inhibits spindle fibre formation in dividing cells. As a result, chromosomes do not move to the poles and tetraploids are often formed.

Gene technology

Gene technology involves the manipulation of genetic material so that, for example, the genetic material of cells can be altered by inserting genes from another organism. Such altered genetic material is referred to as recombinant DNA. Many of the techniques used in gene technology were originally developed using bacteria, particularly *Escherichia coli* (*E. coli*), and enable the insertion of mammalian genes into bacterial cells. This may result in the large-scale production of proteins in bacterial cultures. The first of these to be licensed for human use was insulin, in 1982.

The basis of recombinant DNA technology was established in the 1970s, with the discovery of several enzymes that enable DNA molecules to be cut, copied and joined. These enzymes include restriction endonucleases (type II), DNA ligase and reverse transcriptase.

Restriction endonucleases are extracted from microorganisms. They get their name because they 'restrict' invasion of the host cell by foreign DNA molecules, such as viral DNA, by cutting it up. These enzymes cut at sites within the foreign DNA, rather than removing bases from the ends, so they are called endonucleases, as opposed to exonucleases. Hundreds of different restriction endonucleases have now been isolated and type II restriction enzymes are particularly useful because they cut DNA molecules at specific nucleotide sequences, known as recognition sites. Two such enzymes are known as Eco RI and Hind III, which cut DNA at the specific recognition sites (see Figure 7.10).

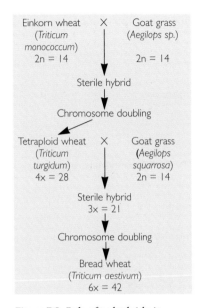

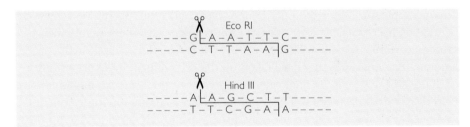

Figure 7.10 Recognition sites on viral DNA for restriction endonucleases Eco RI and Hind III

Notice that each enzyme makes a staggered cut, leaving two complementary ends. These complementary ends have a natural affinity for each other, and are referred to as 'sticky ends'.

Plasmids

Bacterial cells contain small, circular loops of DNA in addition to their circular chromosomal DNA. These small loops of DNA are known as plasmids and sometimes contain a gene that confers resistance to an antibiotic. Plasmids are widely used in gene technology because of their relatively small size and their ability to replicate within the bacterial cell. Plasmids are used as **vectors** to introduce a gene of interest into a host cell. Once in the host cell, the plasmid will replicate so that many copies of the original gene will be produced in each cell.

Figure 7.9 Role of polyploidy in origin of modern hexaploid cultivated wheat Triticum aestivum

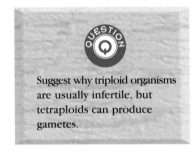

Suggest why triploid organisms are usually infertile, but tetraploids can produce gametes.

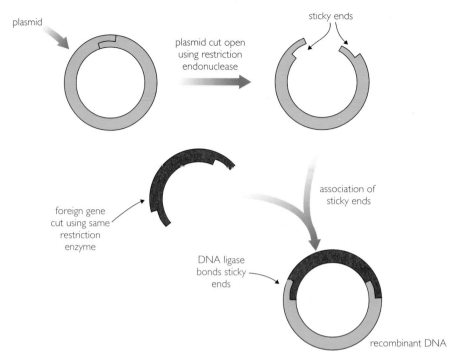

Figure 7.11 Formation of recombinant DNA from a bacterial plasmid acting as a vector for a 'foreign' gene, such as the gene for human insulin

Plasmids can be cut open using a restriction endonuclease and, if a gene is cut out using the same restriction enzyme, they will have complementary sticky ends. This means that the gene and the plasmid will join easily by hydrogen bonding between complementary bases. An enzyme called DNA ligase will join the gene and the plasmid permanently by forming covalent phosphodiester bonds (Figure 7.11).

The recombinant DNA is then placed into bacterial cells. This can be achieved by treating bacterial cells with calcium ions, which makes their membranes more permeable, so they will take up DNA if it is added to their growth medium. Bacterial cells that have taken up the recombinant DNA are referred to as transformed cells. Treated cells are spread out on a suitable medium in a Petri dish so that each cell will grow into a separate colony, or clone. Some of these cells will contain the vector only, if the plasmid has failed to take up the foreign DNA, and others will contain the gene of interest.

One method of finding these cells involves the use of a radioactive DNA probe, containing part of the sequence of the gene required. This probe is used to find cells that have DNA which can hybridise with this probe. These cells are then subcultured to provide a pure culture of transformed cells, which can be grown on a large scale (up to 10 000 dm^3) in industrial fermenters. Bacteria multiply quickly and can be grown in relatively cheap media. The transformed cells will synthesise the protein product, which is then extracted from the cells. Another method for selecting transformed cells involves the use of antibiotics. Plasmids may contain a gene that confers resistance to a particular antibiotic, such as ampicillin. Bacteria that have taken up this plasmid will be able to grow on a medium containing antibiotic and can therefore be selected.

The insulin story

To illustrate a practical and commercially important aspect of gene technology, we will consider the production of human insulin from genetically engineered bacterial cells. Insulin is a relatively small protein molecule, containing 51 amino acid residues. The molecule consists of two chains, an A-chain containing 21 amino acid residues and a B-chain of 30 amino acid residues, held together by two disulphide bonds (Figure 7.12).

Insulin is normally produced by cells in the pancreas and is involved in the regulation of blood glucose. It acts by stimulating the uptake of glucose into muscle and fat cells and therefore reduces the concentration of glucose in the blood. The disease diabetes mellitus is characterised by a high blood glucose concentration, which results from a decreased ability of cells to take up glucose. This is often due to a deficiency in insulin, which may arise from the inability of the sufferers to synthesise normal insulin. These cases can be treated by regular injections of insulin which, for many years, was extracted from pig pancreas. However, two major problems arose, which indicated the need for an alternative source:

- pig insulin causes an immune response in some diabetics
- there was an insufficient supply of animal pancreases.

One approach to producing insulin from genetically modified bacteria was to synthesise the A and B-chains separately. This involved constructing entirely synthetic genes for the A and B-chains.

These synthetic genes were then inserted separately into plasmids. Transformation of *E. coli* by these recombinant plasmids resulted in clones of bacteria capable of producing either the A-chain or the B-chain of human insulin. These chains were extracted from the bacterial cells, purified and mixed in such a way that disulphide bonds were formed.

Human insulin ('Humulin') produced by genetically modified bacteria was the first health product to be produced on a large scale by a process involving recombinant DNA.

Reverse transcriptase

Reverse transcriptase is an enzyme that was first isolated from viruses in 1970. This enzyme will form DNA from an RNA template. This allows complementary, or copy, DNA (cDNA) to be formed from an extract of mRNA. The outline of this process is shown in Figure 7.13.

The double-stranded cDNA sequences are useful in gene technology because they can be inserted into a suitable plasmid vector, which can then be used to transform bacterial cells.

Applications of gene technology

The ability to synthesise a specific protein in large quantities has considerable medical, industrial and agricultural potential. A number of such proteins produced by recombinant DNA technology and now in routine use include

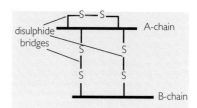

Figure 7.12 Structure of the hormone insulin, showing the two polypeptide chains linked by disulphide bridges

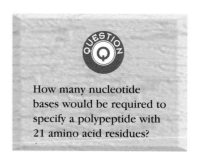

How many nucleotide bases would be required to specify a polypeptide with 21 amino acid residues?

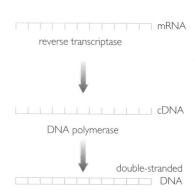

Figure 7.13 Use of enzymes reverse transcriptase and DNA polymerase in production of double-stranded DNA from a mRNA template

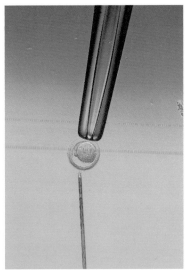

Figure 7.14 Micromanipulation of DNA by injection into nucleus of fertilised host animal ovum

insulin, human growth hormone, erythropoietin (a growth factor secreted by the kidneys that stimulates the production of red blood cells and is used in the treatment of certain types of anaemia), blood clotting factors and bovine growth hormone, or bovine somatotrophin (BST).

Transgenic organisms

Multicellular organisms which contain a foreign gene (that is, from another organism) are referred to as **transgenic**. The technique for producing transgenic animals was developed in mice and involves the microinjection of DNA into a pronucleus of a fertilised ovum (Figure 7.14). A fertilised ovum contains two pronuclei, one from the sperm and one from the egg. The pronuclei will fuse to form the nucleus of the zygote. The ovum containing a foreign gene (known as a transgene) is then implanted into the uterus of a foster mother.

Procedures are being developed to produce transgenic animals such as cows, pigs and sheep. The potential commercial benefits of this technology are considerable, because farm animals may be able to grow larger on smaller amounts of food, or be resistant to certain diseases. Transgenic mammals have been produced that secrete valuable pharmaceutical products in their milk. These include transgenic sheep that produce α-1-antitrypsin, which has potential in the treatment of emphysema, a lung disease, and transgenic pigs that secrete factor IX, which is required for normal blood clotting.

Transgenic plants are also being developed, which may have a significant impact on agriculture throughout the world. For example, some strains of the soil bacterium *Bacillus thuringiensis* produce proteins that selectively bind to the epithelial cells in the intestine of certain insects. This destroys the cells, and liquids in the gut diffuse into the blood and the insect dies. These proteins, known either as δ-endotoxins or T-toxins, are harmless to vertebrates. A gene for one T-toxin has been successfully cloned into maize and tomato plants and shown to confer protection against certain insect pests (Figures 7.15, 7.16).

DNA extracted from *Bacillus thuringiensis*
↓
DNA cut into gene-sized pieces using restriction endonuclease
↓
Identify T–toxin gene by base sequence
↓
Gene transferred to tomato cells grown in tissue culture
↓
Cells containing the T–toxin gene divide
↓
Tomato plantlets regenerated from cell culture
↓
Plantlet grown into mature tomato plant that produces its own T–toxin

Figure 7.15 Procedure for the transfer of the T-toxin gene from the bacterium Bacillus thuringiensis *to tomato plants in order to protect them from insect attack*

Figure 7.16 Genetically modified plants are grown from cell culture in carefully controlled environments

Gene therapy

Gene therapy means the transfer of new genetic material to the cells of an individual, which results in therapeutic benefit to that individual. This has potential for the treatment of genetic diseases. At present, techniques are being developed to insert normal genes into individuals suffering from familial hypercholesterolaemia, and to treat cancer by genetic modification of tumour cells in order to make them more susceptible to attack by the body's immune system.

Social considerations

In the early 1970s, when techniques for gene technology were being developed, there was considerable concern about the safety of the experiments. This led, in 1976, to the introduction of a set of regulations for recombinant DNA research and any experiments that were obviously dangerous were forbidden. It now appears that some of the early fears were unfounded and that there are obvious benefits to the health and well-being of humans. Nevertheless, there are a number of social, ethical and legal considerations that must be faced as new techniques in genetic engineering become available. For example, human growth hormone produced by recombinant DNA technology is now routinely prescribed to increase the growth of abnormally short children. Should athletes use this hormone to try to increase their size and physical performance? Should gene therapy be used to correct inherited defects in body cells, or should it also be used to alter genes in eggs and sperm, so that the corrected genes are transmitted to successive generations? Advances in gene technology clearly raise many questions for which there are no easy answers.

Examination questions

Chapter 1

1 The diagram below shows a model of part of a plasma membrane.

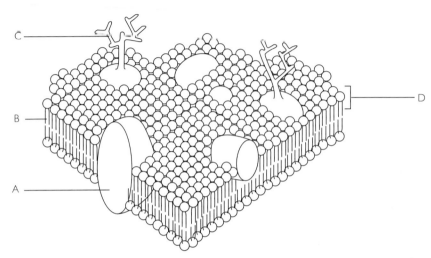

(a) Name the parts labelled A, B, C and D.   (4 marks)

(b) State *one* function of part C.   (1 mark)

(Total 5 marks)

2 The drawing below shows a leaf palisade cell as revealed by an electron microscope.

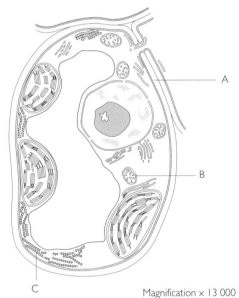

Magnification x 13 000

(a) Name the parts labelled A, B and C.   (3 marks)

(b) Describe *two* ways in which the structure of a prokaryotic cell would differ from that of the cell shown above.   (2 marks)

(Total 5 marks)

Chapter 2

1 Complete the table below, giving the chemical nature and *one* function of the carbohydrates glycogen, ribose and sucrose. The information for starch has been given for you as an example.

Carbohydrate	Chemical nature	*One* function
Starch	Polysaccharide	Carbohydrate storage in plants
Glycogen		
Ribose		
Sucrose		

(Total 6 marks)

2 Give an account of the occurrence and functions of triglycerides in plants and humans.

(Total 10 marks)

Chapter 3

1 Catalase is an enzyme which catalyses the breakdown of the toxic chemical hydrogen peroxide into water and oxygen. The enzyme is found in many tissues including those of potato tubers.

An investigation was carried out into the effect of pH on the rate of catalase activity in potato tuber tissue. The apparatus used in the investigation is shown below.

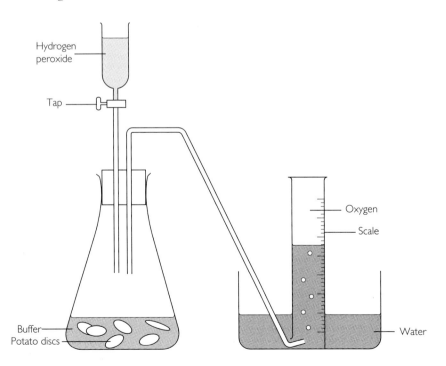

(a)   (i)   Suggest *three* suitable pH values for the experiment and give a reason for your choice. (2 marks)

        (ii)   State *two* conditions, other than pH, which should be kept constant during the experiment. (2 marks)

(b)   (i)   Describe how the apparatus would be used to measure the rate of catalase activity. (4 marks)

        (ii)   Suggest *two* sources of error which could occur during the experiment. (2 marks)

(c)   Suggest why catalase is present in living tissue. (1 mark)

(Total 11 marks)

2   Give an account of the structure and functions of enzymes in living organisms.

(Total 10 marks)

Chapter 4

1   The diagram below shows some of the stages of anaerobic respiration in a yeast cell.

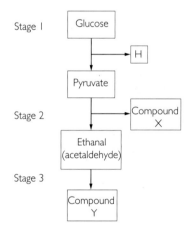

(a)   (i)   Identify compound X, produced at stage 2. (1 mark)
        (ii)   Identify compound Y, produced by stage 3. (1 mark)

(b)   State what happens to the hydrogen atoms produced by stage 1. (2 marks)

(c)   Name *two* products of anaerobic respiration in muscle. (2 marks)

(Total 6 marks)

2   An experiment was carried out to investigate the effect of temperature on anaerobic respiration in yeast cells. Respiring yeast cells were incubated at different temperatures in a sucrose solution to which methylene blue, a redox indicator, had been added. At intervals during each investigation, the light absorbance of the suspension was measured using a colorimeter. The results of the investigation are shown in the graph below.

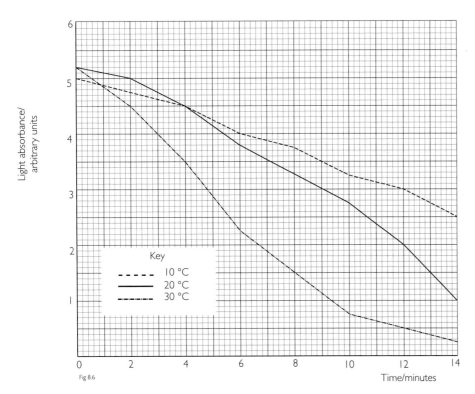

Fig 8.6

Light absorbance/arbitrary units (y-axis)

Time/minutes (x-axis)

Key
- - - - - 10 °C
——— 20 °C
—·—·— 30 °C

(a) (i)   Explain the role of redox indicators such as methylene blue
           in experiments of this kind.   (3 marks)

     (ii) State and explain *one* precaution that should be taken when
           carrying out this experiment, to ensure that the results are
           reliable.   (2 marks)

(b) (i)   Compare the rates of yeast respiration at the three
           temperatures investigated in this experiment.   (3 marks)

     (ii) Explain why temperature should affect the rate of respiration
           of yeast cells in this way.   (3 marks)

                                                    (Total 11 marks)

Chapter 5

1   Read through the following account of protein synthesis, then write on the
    dotted lines the most appropriate word or words to complete the account.

    During protein synthesis, amino acids are linked by ....

    to form polypeptides. This process occurs at the ribosomes. The function

    of the ribosome is to hold the.. in such a way that its

    .... can be recognised and paired with the

    complementary .... in the t-RNA. The molecules

    manufactured by ribosomes situated on the .... of the

    cell may be converted to glycoproteins in the ....

                                                    (Total 6 marks)

2   The table below refers to events in the process of mitosis and the first division of meiosis (meiosis I).

If the statement is correct, place a tick (✔) in the appropriate box and if the statement is incorrect place a cross (✗) in the appropriate box.

Feature	Mitosis	Meiosis I
Formation of spindle occurs		
Homologous chromosomes pair up		
Separation of chromatids occurs		
Formation of chiasmata		
Condensation of chromosomes		

(Total 5 marks)

Chapter 6

1   Sickle cell anaemia is an autosomal recessive genetic defect.

The diagram below shows the pedigree of a family affected by sickle cell anaemia. (Individuals are numbered 1, 2, 3, 4, etc. to 12.)

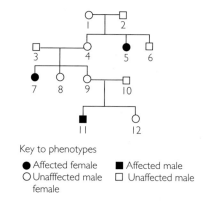

Key to phenotypes

● Affected female   ■ Affected male
○ Unafffected male   □ Unaffected male
female

(a)   State the numbers of all the individuals in the pedigree that are certain to be heterozygous for this gene.   (3 marks)

(b)   What is the probability that individual 6 is heterozygous for this gene?   (1 mark)

(c)   The parasite which causes malaria digests haemoglobin in the red blood cells (erythrocytes). Suggest why individuals heterozygous for this gene may show increased resistance to malaria.   (2 marks)

(Total 6 marks)

2   Maize cobs may have purple or red grains. This character is controlled by a single pair of alleles. The dominant allele **A** gives a purple colour and the recessive allele **a** gives a red colour.

(a)   In an experiment, a heterozygous plant is crossed with a maize plant homozygous for the allele **a**. State the genotypes of these two plants. (1 mark)

(b)   Grain colour is also affected by a second pair of alleles. The presence of the dominant alle **E** allows the purple colour to develop, but in the homozygous recessive (**ee**) no colour will develop (despite the presence of alleles **A** or **a**) and the grain will be white. A plant of genotype **AAEE** is crossed with a plant of genotype **aaee**.

(i)   State the genotype and phenotype of the offspring produced as a result of this cross. (2 marks)

(ii)   The plants of the offspring are allowed to self-fertilise. Draw a genetic diagram to show the possible genotypes produced as a result of this cross. (3 marks)

(iii)   Predict the phenotypic ratio that would be obtained from this cross. (3 marks)

(iv)   Which genotypes, if allowed to self-fertilise, would produce pure-breeding lines containing white grains? (3 marks)

(Total 12 marks)

Chapter 7

1   The base sequences from two strands of DNA are shown in the diagram below. The two sequences are from the same section of a chromosome: the first is the normal sequence and the second is a mutant form.

normal DNA   AATCAGGTTA
mutant DNA   ATACCAGTTA

(a)   Describe and name *two* point mutations in the mutant DNA. (2 marks)

(b)   After transcription, a strand of mRNA is produced. Write the mRNA sequence which would be produced from the mutant DNA. (1 mark)

(c)   (i)   Describe how the polypeptide chain produced from this mRNA sequence may differ from the normal polypeptide. (1 mark)

(ii)   Suggest how this may affect the activity of the polypeptide. (2 marks)

(Total 6 marks)

EXAMINATION QUESTIONS

2   Read through the following passage on gene technology (genetic engineering), then write on the dotted lines the most appropriate word or words to complete the passage.

The isolation of specific genes during a genetic engineering process involves forming eukaryotic DNA fragments. These fragments are formed using .... enzymes which make staggered cuts in the DNA within specific base sequences. This leaves single-stranded 'sticky ends' at each end. The same enzyme is used to open up a circular loop of bacterial DNA which acts as a .... for the eukaryotic DNA. The complementary sticky ends of the bacterial DNA are joined to the DNA fragment using another enzyme called .... DNA fragments can also be made from .... template. Reverse transcriptase is used to produce a single strand of DNA and the enzyme .... catalyses the formation of a double helix. Finally new DNA is introduced into host .... cells. These can then be cloned on an industrial scale and large amounts of protein harvested. An example of a protein currently manufactured using this technique is ....

(Total 7 marks)

Mark schemes

In the mark schemes, the following symbols are used.
; indicates separate marking points
/ indicates alternative marking points
eq means correct equivalent points are accepted

Chapter 1

1   (*a*)   A = protein ;
             B = lipid/fatty acid/hydrophobic chain ;
             C = carbohydrate/glycocalyx ;
             D = phospholipid;   (4 marks)

    (*b*)   recognition/binding sites/receptors/cell adhesion;

                                           (1 mark)
                                   (Total 5 marks)

2   (*a*)   A = cell wall ;
             B = mitochondrion ;
             C = rough endoplasmic reticulum/ribosome;   (3 marks)

    (*b*)   (a prokaryotic cell has) two of: no true nucleus/no nuclear membrane/no nucleolus/no membrane bound organelles/no mitochondria/no chloroplasts/no endoplasmic reticulum/no Golgi apparatus/no large vacuole/no starch/no cellulose cell wall/smaller ribosomes;   (2 marks)

                                     (Total 5 marks)

Chapter 2

1

Carbohydrate	Chemical nature	One function
Glycogen	Polysaccharide;	Carbohydrate storage in animals/liver/muscle;
Ribose	Monosaccharide/ pentose;	Constituent of RNA/ATP/NAD;
Sucrose	Disaccharide;	Transport/storage in plants;

(Total 6 marks)

triglycerides as energy stores; ref. to heavily reduced nature/hydrogen content; suitable stores because they are insoluble in/immiscible with water; thus metabolically inert; enter metabolism only after hydrolysis ; ref. to high energy content per unit mass ; occurrence in seeds ; link with lightness for dispersal; rare in vegetative plant stores; subcutaneous fat in humans; specified location; link with lightness for motility; formation of metabolic water on oxidation/respiration; importance in desert species/ ref. to camel hump; etc;

(Total 10 marks)

Chapter 3

1   (a)   (i)   pH 3, 7, 10/eq; one acid, one neutral, one basic/over wide pH range;   (2 marks)

      (ii)   temperature; volume of buffer; volume/concentration of hydrogen peroxide; number/mass/surface area of potato discs;   (2 marks)

   (b)   (i)   use freshly cut potato tissue/fresh tissue/same potato/equilibration of solutions/discs to temperature/pH; add peroxide and close tap/collect oxygen for particular time/note the time for production of a standard volume of oxygen/count the number of bubbles in a give time; read volume collected off scale; rate = volume divided by time/rate = number of bubbles divided by time; replication with same buffer; calculate mean rate of oxygen production at each pH/plot a graph and find slope;   (4 marks)

      (ii)   concentration of catalase in discs may vary; it is hard to get the same surface area of potato discs; frothing may affect oxygen collection; volume of peroxide added may displace air into collection chamber; volume of gas depends on temperature/pressure; oxygen may escape/apparatus may leak; bubbles may stick to the potato;   (2 marks)

   (c)   catalase breaks down toxic hydrogen peroxide produced in metabolism;   (1 mark)

(Total 11 marks)

2   enzymes consist of chains of amino acids; forming polypeptides; enzymes are globular proteins; ref. to active site; substrate fits into active site/induced fit reference; active site is the site of reaction/formation of products; enzymes are specific; their structure can be altered by temperature/pH; they are often associated with prosthetic groups; enzymes speed up the reactions/act as catalysts; lower activation energy; function best at optimum temperature; they enable reactions to take place within cells/organisms within suitable temperature limits; function best at optimum pH; enzymes are reusable/not changed/enzymes control metabolic pathways; example of anabolism; example of catabolism;

(Total 10 marks)

Chapter 4

1 (a) (i)   carbon dioxide/CO_2;   (1 mark)

   (ii)   ethanal;   (1 mark)

   (b)   picked up by NAD; used to reduce ethanal/produce ethanol;

                                                            (2 marks)

   (c)   ATP; lactate; heat;   (2 marks)

                                                      (Total 6 marks)

2 (a) (i)   redox indicators act as hydrogen acceptors; they change
               colour when reduced/methylene blue changes from blue to
               colourless; rate of change indicates the rate of reaction;
               dehydrogenase enzymes are involved;   (3 marks)

   (ii)   use same quantity of yeast/same batch of yeast/same
          concentration of sucrose/same volume of indicator/same
          volume of sample used in colorimeter/each temperature kept
          constant;

          to ensure that the results are comparable;   (2 marks)

   (b) (i)   rate is highest at 30 °C/slowest at 10 °C; fastest rate up to
               10 minutes at 30 °C; 10 °C and 20 °C curves follow similar
               patterns/steady rate; reaction nearly completed by 14
               minutes at 30 °C;   (3 marks)

   (ii)   respiration is enzyme dependent; increase in temperature
          results in an increase in enzyme activity; increases the
          movement of molecules; more enzyme-substrate complexes
          formed/increases the chances of collision; 10 °C rise
          doubles the rate of reaction;   (3 marks)

                                                     (Total 11 marks)

Chapter 5

1 peptide bonds; mRNA; codons; anticodons; endoplasmic reticulum; Golgi
   apparatus;

                                                      (Total 6 marks)

Feature	Mitosis	Meiosis I
Formation of spindle occurs	✔	✔
Homologous chromosomes pair up	✗	✔
Separation of chromatids occurs	✔	✗
Formation of chiasmata	✗	✔
Condensation of chromosomes	✔	✔

                                                      (Total 5 marks)

Chapter 6

1   (a)   1, 2, 3, 4, 9, 10;   (3 marks)

      (b)   66%/⅔/0.66;   (1 mark)

      (c)   (sickling) may stop parasite binding/entering cell; mixture of haemoglobins in red blood cells/different amino acid in HbS; parasites cannot digest HbS/sickle cells have less haemoglobin; parasites fail to reproduce/die;

                                                                      (2 marks)
                                                              (Total 6 marks)

2   (a)   **Aa** and **aa**;   (1 mark)

      (b)   (i)   Genotype: **AaEe**;
                      Phenotype: purple grains;   (2 marks)

          (ii)

gametes	AE	Ae	aE	ae
AE	AAEE	AAEe	AaEE	AaEe
Ae	AAEe	AAee	AaEe	Aaee
aE	AaEE	AaEe	aaEE	aaEe
ae	AaEe	Aaee	aaEe	aaee

                                                                             (3 marks)

         (iii)   purple; 4 white; 3 red;   (3 marks)

         (iv)   **AAee**; **Aaee**; **aaee**;   (3 marks)
                                                              (Total 12 marks)

Chapter 7

1   (a)   inversion of T and A; insertion/addition of C; deletion of G; substitution of C for A; substitution of A for G;   (2 marks)

      (b)   UAUGGUCAAU;   (1 mark)

      (c)   (i)   the amino acid sequence will be changed/eq;   (1 mark)

         (ii)   amino acid sequence affects the 3D/secondary/tertiary structure of polypeptide; if an enzyme, changes the shape of the active site; enzyme/protein may no longer function; reference to a qualified example, such as haemoglobin may no longer carry oxygen;   (2 marks)
                                                               (Total 6 marks)

2   restriction endonuclease; vector/carrier; ligase; mRNA; polymerase; yeast/bacterial/prokaryotic; insulin/GH/interferon/eq;

                                                                        (Total 7 marks)

Index

immune system 109
independent assortment 76, 88, 100
induced fit 38
inhibitors 41
 irreversible 41
 reversible 41
insertion mutation 101
insulin 105, 107, 108
introns 63
inulin 28
ions
 anions 20
 cations 20
isomerism 23
 structural 23
Kendrew and Perutz 34
keratin 32
ketone groups 23
kidney 16
Krebs, Sir Hans 7, 48
Krebs cycle 7, 48, 50–52, 53

lactate 54
lamellae 7
 middle 9, 71
 see also thylakoids
ligase 105–6
lignification 9
lignin 9
link reaction 51, 53
linkage 90–92
 partial 92
lipids 3–5, 8, 20, 29–31
lock and key mechanism 38
lysosomes 5–6

meiosis 68–77, 100
Mendel, Gregor 80, 85, 88
mesophyll
 palisade 1
mesosome 11
messenger RNA (mRNA) 101, 102
metabolic pathway 41–42, 48
metabolism 16, 19, 41
 anabolic reactions 19
 catabolic reactions 19
metaphase 70–77, 73, 74
methionine 62
microfibrils 8
 see cellulose
microfilaments 11
micropinocytic vesicles 17
microtubules 8, 11, 70
microvilli 17
minimal medium 59–60
mitochondria 2, 6, 7, 10, 50–52
mitosis 68–77
molecules
 dipolar 19–20
 lipid 3
 organic 21
 polar 19–20
 polysaccharide 4, 8
 protein 3
monocytes 17
monohybrid inheritance 82–86
monosaccharides 22
monosomy 103
mucopolysaccharides 29
murein 10, 28
muscle 54
mutagen 101
mutation 60, 100
mutation rate 100

neutrophils 17
Nicolson, 3–4
nicotinamide adenine dinucleotide
 (NAD$^+$) 49–52
nicotinamide adenine dinucleotide
 phosphate (NADP$^+$) 49
non-disjunction 103–4
nuclear division 6, 66–69
nuclear envelope 2, 6, 9–10, 63
nuclear pores 6
nucleic acids 12, 35–37, 101
nucleolar organisers 66
nucleoli 6, 69
nucleoplasm 6
nucleosides 35
nucleosomes 56
nucleotide 35–6, 48, 56–79
nucleus 1–3, 6, 6–7, 9–10

octamer 56
one gene–one enzyme hypothesis
 60
one gene–one protein hypothesis
 60
operon 66
operator region
optimum pH 40
optimum temperature 39–40
organelles 2–9, 13, 69
organisms
 multicellular 1
 unicellular 1
 heterozygous 83
 homozygous 83
organs 1
osmometer 15
osmosis 13, 15–16
oxaloacetate 51
oxidative phosporylation 48, 52–53
oxygen debt 54

pancreatic juice 46
Parvovirus 12
pectates 9
pectins 8, 28
pentoses 23
peptides 10
peptide bonds 31, 64
peptidoglycan 10
permeability
 partial (or selective) 13, 15
phagocytosis 17
phenotype 82, 86–7, 100
phenylketonuria 59
phosphate 48
phosphate groups 56
phosphodiester bonds 35
phosphoester 35
phosphoglucose isomerase 42
phosphoric acid 35
phosphorylation 49
phospholipids 4, 29–31
 polar and non-polar portions of
 4
 hydrophilia in 4–5
 hydrophobia in 4–5, 13–15
photosynthesis 8, 32
phototrophic organism 48
phragmoplast 71
pigments 7
pili 11
 see also fimbriae
pinocytosis 17
plasma membrane 3
plasmids 11, 105–6, 107

plasmodesma 9, 71
plastids 7
point mutation 101
polymerases 56–7
polymers 25
polynucleotide chains 59, 69
polypeptide chains 32
polyploidy 67, 103, 104
polysaccharides 25–29
polysomes 64, 65
polysomy 103
principle of segregation 84
Prokaryotae 8, 9–11
promoter region 66
prophase 70–77, 73, 74
proteins 3–4, 5, 14–15, 31–35, 38
 extrinsic 5
 glucose transporter 16
 intrinsic 5
 synthesis of 7, 32, 57, 62–66
 transport 14
protein coat (viruses) 12
Protoctista 8
proton (H$^+$)
protozoa 8, 17
Punnett square 89
purines 36
pyrimidines 36
pyranose 23
pyruvate 49, 50

reactions
 (in metabolism) anabolic 19
 (in metabolism) catabolic 19
 (in photosynthesis) light-
 dependent 8
 (in photosynthesis) light-
 independent 8
 condensation 24
 exergonic 39, 48
 exothermic 39
reactive groups 23
reciprocal translocation 103
recognition site 105
recombinant DNA 105–6
recombinants 89–99
recombination 89, 100
redox indicator 55
reduction division 69
replication forks 59
repressor molecule 65
residues (monosaccharide) 24
respiration
 aerobic 7, 11, 13
respiratory substrate 27
restriction endonuclease 105, 108
reverse transcriptase 105–107
riboses 23, 48
ribosomes 2, 5–6, 10–11
ribozyme 38
RNA (ribonucleic acid) 6, 12, 23
 messenger 62
 ribosomal 62
 transfer 62
RNA polymerase 62

Saccharomyces cervisiae 1
saliva 46
scaffold protein 56
secondary constrictions 66
 see also nucleolar organisers
segregation 100
semi-conservative replication 58–59
sex determination 95
sex linkage 95

sex linked traits 96
sexual reproduction 68
sickle-cell anaemia 86, 102
Singer, 3–4
slime layer 10
sodium pump 16
sodium–potassium pump 16
spindle (in nuclear division) 8,
 70–77
spiralisation 70
sporophyte 68
starch 8, 26–27
stereoisomerism 24
steroid hormones 5
sticky ends 105
stroma 7–8
substitution mutation 101, 102
substrate 38
succinate dihydrogenase 41
sucrose 21
sugars
 reducing and non-reducing 25
sugar–phosphate backbone 57

T-toxin 108
telophase 70–77, 73, 74
test cross 85, 92
 see also back cross
thalassaemia 87
thylakoids 7–8, 11
 see also lamellae
thymine 36, 57
tissues 1
tobacco mosaic virus 12
transcription 62–66
transformation 106
transformed cells 106
transgene 108
transgenic animal 108
transgenic plant 108
translation 62, 63–66
translocation mutation 103–104
tricarboxylic acid (TCA) 7, 51
 cycle 51
trioses 23
triphenyl tetrazolium chloride
 (TTC) 55
triplet code 60
triploid 104
trisomy 103
trypsin 43
tubulin 8
tumour cells 109

uracil 36, 101

variation 80, 100
 continuous 80–82
 discontinuous 80–82
vector 105
viruses 12
 as akaryotes 12
 as parasites 12

water, roles of 19–21
Watson, James 57
Wilkins, Maurice 57
wheat (Triticum aestivum) 67, 104
wine 54

X-ray diffraction patterns 57
xylem 9, 21

yeast 1, 53–54